PRENTICE HALL
LITERATURE
Timeless Voices, Timeless Themes

TEACHER'S EDITION

Vocabulary and Spelling Practice Book

WORLD MASTERPIECES

OBSOLETE

PEARSON

Prentice
Hall

Upper Saddle River, New Jersey
Needham, Massachusetts

ISBN 0-13-180386-7

2 3 4 5 6 7 8 9   06

Contents

Name _____ Date _____

Vocabulary Practice 1: Prefixes

Prefixes: *ig-, il-, im-, in-, ir-*

A **prefix** is a word part added to the beginning of a base word that changes the word's meaning. Knowing a prefix's meaning can help you determine the meaning of a new word.

The prefix *in-* means "not." Adding *in-* to the word *appropriate*, meaning "suitable" or "proper," makes *inappropriate*, which means "not appropriate." The prefixes *ig-, il-, im-,* and *ir-* also mean "not."

A. Add the word that belongs with each prefix to make the new word that matches the definition. Use a dictionary to check your work.

mutable	audible	coherent	relevant	partial
eligible	literate	noble	reverent	reparable

1. in _____ means "not able to be heard"

2. in _____ means "not logically connected or understandable"

3. ig _____ means "not of high moral character"

4. im _____ means "not favoring one person or side"

5. ir _____ means "not able to be fixed"

6. in _____ means "not qualified or worthy"

7. il _____ means "not able to read and write"

8. im _____ means "not changeable"

9. ir _____ means "not respectful"

10. ir _____ means "not related to the matter at hand"

B. Write the word from Exercise A that best completes each sentence.

1. Some scientists believe that humans have caused _____ damage to our planet.

2. When the microphone broke, the singer's voice became _____.

3. A funeral is no place for _____, or otherwise disrespectful behavior.

4. The crowd was baffled by the mayor's rambling, _____ speech.

5. The talent show judge found it difficult to be fair and _____ when her favorite nephew took the stage and began his tuba performance.

6. The soldier stood accused of fleeing the battlefield and other _____ acts.

7. The judge's code of ethics was _____. She could never be swayed from it.

8. The _____ man could not read a bedtime story to his daughter.

9. Dancing skills are _____ to the requirements of an accountant's job.

10. Sandy is _____ for the soccer team because of her failing grades.

Name _____ Date _____

Vocabulary Practice 2: Prefixes

Prefixes: *mal-, male-, mis-*

A **prefix** is a word part added to the beginning of a base word that changes the word's meaning. Knowing a prefix's meaning can help you determine the meaning of a new word.

The prefix *mis-* means "badly" or "wrongly." Adding *mis-* to the word *inform*, meaning "to give knowledge of something," makes *misinform*, which means "inform wrongly." The prefixes *mal-* and *male-* mean "bad," "wrong," or "poor."

A. Underline the words in these sentences with the prefixes meaning "badly," "wrongly," "bad," "wrong," or "poor."

1. The medical malpractice case destroyed the physician's reputation.

2. Even after winning the lawsuit, the malcontent still claimed he was cheated.

3. Under our town's new curfew law, anyone outside after midnight will be charged with a misdemeanor.

4. Scientists made a miscalculation and the rocket flew into the ocean.

5. The maladroit chef dropped the birthday cake onto the celebrant's lap.

6. "The Best in the West" was definitely a misnomer for the dirty, run-down motel.

7. The foreign exchange student misinterpreted the teacher and missed graduation.

8. A faulty compass caused the Boy Scouts a misadventure in the park.

9. Large clouds of black smoke indicated that our car engine was malfunctioning.

10. Melvin's model airplane looked more like a misshapen lump of plastic.

B. For each underlined word, write the prefix and base word beside the definition.

Prefix	Base Word	Definition of the Underlined Word
1. _____	_____	a wrongly applied name
2. _____	_____	deformed
3. _____	_____	understood incorrectly
4. _____	_____	performing work improperly
5. _____	_____	bad behavior
6. _____	_____	unprofessional or improper treatment
7. _____	_____	bad fortune, disaster
8. _____	_____	an incorrect judgment or account
9. _____	_____	awkward, clumsy
10. _____	_____	not satisfied, unhappy

C. Write five more words with the prefixes *mal-, male-,* and *mis-*. Check your words in a dictionary.

Name _____ Date _____

Vocabulary Practice 3: Prefixes

Prefixes: *sym-, syn-, sys-*

A **prefix** is a word part added to the beginning of a base word that changes the word's meaning. Knowing a prefix's meaning can help you determine the meaning of a new word.

The prefix *sym-* means "with." In *sympathy*, the Greek root *-pathy* comes from the root *pathos,* meaning "emotion." Sympathy means "with shared feeling." The prefixes *syn-* and *sys-* also mean "with," "at the same time," or "together."

A. Add the prefix and root to make a new word.

Prefix and Base Word	**New Word**
1. *syn* and *chronize* (time together)	_____
2. *sys* and *temic* (a set of things together)	_____
3. *syn* and *drome* (run together)	_____
4. *sym* and *biotic* (living together)	_____
5. *sym* and *physis* (growing together)	_____
6. *sys* and *tematic* (set together)	_____
7. *sym* and *posium* (meeting together)	_____
8. *sym* and *metry* (measure together)	_____
9. *syn* and *ergy* (work together)	_____
10. *syn* and *thesis* (place, do together)	_____

B. Use the words you formed in Exercise A to complete the sentences.

1. Nitrogen-fixing bacteria and legumes live in a _____ relationship.

2. The _____ of the recycling committee helped them collect the bottles and cans.

3. Looking for clues, the police conducted a _____ search of the building.

4. The chemist toiled all night, but could not achieve a _____ of the compounds.

5. Professor Jenkins joined the other scientists for the biology _____ .

6. After setting the meeting time, the two agents _____ their watches.

7. Calvin's _____ reaction to the bee sting turned his entire body red and itchy.

8. A _____ of the bones in an infant's head forms the solid skull.

9. The doctor diagnosed the problem based on the _____ his patient described.

10. Everyone admired the _____ of the design in the ancient cathedral windows.

C. On other paper, write as many more words as you can with the prefixes *syn-, sys-,* or *sym-.* Use a dictionary to check your words.

Vocabulary Practice 4 : Prefixes

Prefixes: *anti-, counter-, contra-, contro-*

A **prefix** is a word part added to the beginning of a base word that changes the word's meaning. Knowing a prefix's meaning can help you determine the meaning of a new word.

The prefix *counter-* means "against." Adding *counter* to the base word *clockwise,* meaning "in the direction of the clock," makes *counterclockwise,* which means "in the opposite direction of the clock." The prefixes *anti-, contra-,* and *contro-* also mean "against," "the opposite of," or "opposed to."

A. Add a word or word part to the prefix to make a new word that matches the definition.

charged indication	-diction -versy	productive thesis	climax measures	sign intelligence

Prefix	Base Word	New Word	Definition
1. anti-	climax	anticlimax	a sudden drop after rising expectations
2. contra-	_____	_____	to go against, oppose
3. counter-	_____	_____	causing results opposite those intended
4. contra-	_____	_____	that which makes treatment inadvisable
5. counter-	_____	_____	to give a second, confirming signature
6. anti-	_____	_____	the completely opposite idea
7. counter-	_____	_____	answered to another charge
8. contro-	_____	_____	a quarrel, dispute
9. counter-	_____	_____	opposite actions
10. counter-	_____	_____	actions against espionage

B. Use the ten words you created in Exercise A to complete the sentences.

1. Eating a gallon of ice cream after exercising could be considered _____ .

2. In World War II, _____ protected disclosure of military secrets.

3. The town of Skyville was caught up in a _____ over the new factory's pollution.

4. The short story ended with an _____ that stunned the students.

5. To protest intrusion of its fishing grounds, villagers initiated drastic _____ .

6. Lawyers prepared the documents for the home buyers to _____
   their agreement.

7. Kyle and Mark never agree—one brother's opinion is the _____ of
   the other's.

8. The child's medication was a _____ and caused a life-threatening situation.

9. The tour guide's statement was a _____ of the most recent historical study.

10. The accused angrily _____ the accuser, creating outcries in the courtroom.

Name _____ Date _____

Vocabulary Practice 5 : Suffixes

Suffixes: *-able, -ble, -ible*

A **suffix** is a word part added to a base word that can add to or change the meaning of the word. Most words from Latin and Greek origins are composed of two or more parts whose meanings and spellings have changed over time.

The word *fallible,* which means "able to be mistaken," is the Latin word *fallere* meaning "to deceive" and the suffix *-ible* meaning "capable or able." The suffixes *-able* and *-ble* also mean "capable or able."

A. Combine the word and suffix and write the new word. Then write the definition of the new word.

Meaning/Word	New Word	Definition
1. (fail) *fall* and *ible*	_____	_____
2. (touch) *palp* and *able*	_____	_____
3. (delight) *delect* and *able*	_____	_____
4. (draw out) *exhaust* and *ible*	_____	_____
5. (praise) *laud* and *able*	_____	_____
6. (drink) *pot* and *able*	_____	_____
7. (hear) *aud* and *ible*	_____	_____
8. (bend, fold) *pli* and *able*	_____	_____
9. (roof of mouth) *palat* and *able*	_____	_____
10. (despise) *despic* and *able*	_____	_____

B. Complete the sentences with suffixed words from Exercise A.

1. Finding the defendant's crimes _____, the judge maximized his sentence.

2. We were so thirsty that we drank the water without caring if it was _____ .

3. When our supervisor forgot about the meeting, it proved that she was _____ .

4. My first attempt to cook without a recipe resulted in a very _____ dinner.

5. Patients arrived in the emergency room with _____ bruises.

6. Although the world's oil supply does not appear to be _____, scientists say we could consume it unless we change our habits.

7. The presidential candidate's _____ goal was to meet every U.S. citizen.

8. Two miles away, the music from the outdoor concert was _____ in our backyard.

9. Cardboard and other _____ materials were used to create the out-door scenery.

10. Ms. Henderson's crab cakes were the most _____ dish at the potluck dinner.

Vocabulary Practice 6 : Suffixes

Suffixes: -ous, -some, -ly, -y

A **suffix** is a word part added to the end of a word that changes the meaning of the word. Knowing the meaning of a suffix can help you determine the meaning of a word.

The suffix *-ous* means "full of." Adding *-ous* to the base word *glamour* makes *glamourous*, which means "full of glamour and beauty." The suffixes *-ly, -some,* and *-y* also mean "full of" or "tending to be."

A. Underline the words in these sentences with the suffixes meaning "full of" or "like."

1. When we chopped down the tree, we were surprised to see the pithy stem.

2. Everyone left the lecture quite offended by the acrimonious speaker.

3. The paper we used was thin and porous so the ink we used seeped through.

4. Pianos are the most cumbersome pieces of furniture to move.

5. The house seemed vacuous and deserted after years of happiness.

6. Billowy sails were a pretty sight in the bay as we left the jetty to join them.

7. The pollution habits of some major factories are outright loathsome.

8. Nellie managed the household expenses frugally and saved enough for a trip.

9. I glanced at the precipitous road outside the car window and gasped.

10. In class, we all took notes copiously, which resulted in high exam grades.

B. Write the words you underlined in Exercise A as base words suffixes. Then write the definitions of the words with the suffixes. The first one is an example.

Word/Meaning	Base Word and Suffix	Definition
1. **loath** (detest)	loathe and some	tending to be detestable.
2. **pith** (substance)	_____	_____
3. **precipice** (steep cliff)	_____	_____
4. **frugal** (stingy)	_____	_____
5. **cumber** (hinder)	_____	_____
6. **billow** (swell, surge)	_____	_____
7. **vacuum** (empty)	_____	_____
8. **acrimony** (bitterness)	_____	_____
9. **copious** (abundant)	_____	_____
10. **pore** (tiny opening)	_____	_____

C. On other paper, write two words with each of the suffixes: *-ly, -ous, -some, -y.*

Vocabulary Practice 7 : Suffixes

Suffixes: -ment, -ness, -ship, -tude,

A **suffix** is a word part added to the end of a word that changes the meaning of the word. Knowing the meaning of a suffix can help you determine the meaning of a word.

The suffix -*ment* means "act or state of." Adding -*ment* to the base word *content* makes *contentment*, which means "state of satisfaction." The suffixes -*ment*, -*ness*, -*tude*, and -*ship* mean "act of" or "state or quality of."

A. Write the base or root from the list with the suffix to complete in each sentence.

plati- (dull, flat)	**disband**	**admonish**	**impoverish**	**enhance**
steward	**adroit**	**intern**	**recti-** (right)	**adept**

1. After three weeks of _____ ship at the copy center, Aaron had not learned much.

2. The street performer's _____ ness at juggling fruit entertained audiences.

3. "Better luck next time" was one _____ tude our team was tired of hearing.

4. The _____ ment from our teacher kept us quiet the rest of the afternoon.

5. Students from the small college were known for their high degree of _____ tude.

6. Decorators illustrated how home _____ ment is an asset to selling property.

7. The infant's _____ ness with the mobile impressed the doctors and nurses.

8. The _____ ment of the entire country was the result of years of civil strife.

9. The new dictator called for the complete _____ ment of all opposition parties.

10. _____ ship of the children was given to a relative after they lost their parents.

B. Write the words you created in Exercise A. Then, write the letter of the definition on the line in front of the word. The first one is an example.

	Word	Definition
_g_	1. internship	a. the quality of being flat or dull
____	2. _____	b. being broken up or ceasing to function
____	3. _____	c. the state of being clever
____	4. _____	d. leading straight, strict honesty
____	5. _____	e. act of managing or overseeing
____	6. _____	f. quality of being poor; poverty
____	7. _____	g. being an apprentice
____	8. _____	h. the quality of being made greater or improved
____	9. _____	i. warnings; cautions
____	10. _____	j. act of mental or physical skill

Vocabulary Practice 8: Combining Forms

Combining Form: -logy

A **combining form** is a word part that occurs in compound words or derived words and is combined with other words.

The Latin **combining form** -logy means "study of." Adding -logy to the base word zoo makes zoology, meaning "study of animals."

A. Combine -logy with these word parts to form words.

1. *paleonto-* (prehistoric life forms) _____

2. *ichthyo-* (branch of zoology dealing with fish) _____

3. *phono-* (sound) _____

4. *pharmac-* (drug) _____

5. *ideo-* (idea) _____

6. *socio-* (companion, society) _____

7. *crimino-* (crime) _____

8. *physio-* (nature) _____

9. *immuno-* (immunity) _____

10. *anthropo-* (humans) _____

11. *chrono-* (of time) _____

12. *termino-* (terms) _____

13. *genea-* (race, descent) _____

14. *lexico-* (of words) _____

15. *dermato-* (skin) _____

B. Use these phrases and the definitions in Exercise A to write a sentence about each science or branch of study. Use the boldface words in your sentences. Use a dictionary or encyclopedia, if necessary.

1. **paleontology**—discovers fossils _____

2. **ichthyology**—salmon migration _____

3. **phonology**—sounds of words _____

4. **pharmacology**—antibiotics _____

5. **ideology**—theories or doctrines _____

6. **sociology**—cultural customs _____

7. **criminology**—timeline _____

8. **physiology**—functions of the system _____

9. **immunology**—infectious diseases _____

10. **geneaology**—family tree _____

Vocabulary Practice 9: Word Roots

Word Roots: -cur-, -curr-, -curs-, -pel-, -puls-

A **word root** is a word or group of letters that forms the basic part of a word and gives the word its primary meaning. If you know the meaning of a root form, you can determine the meaning of the whole word.

The Latin roots -cur-, -curr-, and -curs- all mean "run" or "take place." The word *occur*, which means "run," and the word *current*, which means "running now," have the same root. The Latin roots -pel- and -puls- mean "drive" or "push." The words *repel* and *repulse* have roots with the same meaning.

A. Underline the words with the roots listed above. Then, using the root meanings and sentence clues, write definitions for the words you underlined.

1. The picnickers were able to repel the ant invasion and save their lunch.

   _____

2. Trish's tendency to drive over the speed limit was recurrent, so the judge raised the fine.

   _____

3. Lisha felt an overwhelming impulse to put on her running shoes and go for a jog.

   _____

4. My history teacher's meandering, or discursive, lectures leave me daydreaming.

   _____

5. Scientists use solid rocket fuel to propel the space shuttle into orbit.

   _____

6. If you tease a dog, you could incur its wrath and that could be harmful.

   _____

7. Linnea's parents hoped that the promise of a new car would compel her to study.

   _____

8. Reading the curriculum description, Todd decided to enroll for the lecture series.

   _____

9. Andy's expulsion from school did not surprise anyone but his parents.

   _____

10. Willy must make a choice of sports since the soccer and lacrosse seasons are concurrent.

    _____

B. Make a list of other words with the root forms listed above. Identify the roots and write the definitions. Explain how knowing the root meanings helps you determine word meaning.

Vocabulary Practice 10 : Word Roots

Word Roots: -cit-, -dic-, -loc-, -logue-, -loquy-, -loqu-, -voc-

A **word root** is a word or group of letters that forms the basic part of a word and gives the word its primary meaning. If you know the meaning of a root form, you can determine the meaning of the whole word.

The Latin root -voc- means "speak," "talk," or "say," as in vocation, which means "a calling," and vocalize, which means "speak" or "sing." Other roots with the same meaning are -cit-, -dic-, and -loqu-. Roots -logue- and -loquy- mean "speech" or "writing."

A. Underline the words with the roots listed above. Then, circle the word that defines the word you underlined.

1. The store catalogue is always colorful, detailed, and popular with customers.
   a. brochure   b. order form   c. inventory

2. Everyone left the auditorium inspired by the speaker's eloquent lecture.
   a. quiet   b. humorous   c. well-spoken

3. Jake is loquacious on the telephone, so I can walk away and return minutes later.
   a. difficult   b. talkative   c. forgetful

4. The babysitter was forced to call the vociferous child's parents at the restaurant.
   a. sleepy   b. mischievous   c. noisy

5. The convocation of honors students was very impressive and inspirational.
   a. assembly   b. graduation   c. address

6. Many writers believe that a book's prologue should carry an important message.
   a. dedication   b. introduction   c. conclusion

7. Most late night talk show hosts begin with a monologue about current events.
   a. parody   b. speech   c. dramatization

8. My father followed the scuffle with a dictum about sibling behavior.
   a. declaration   b. opinion   c. decision

9. Many colonists regarded the king's edict concerning taxes to be unacceptable.
   a. charter   b. order   c. reign

10. A letter written in a colloquial style is fine for friends, but not for business letters.
    a. old-fashioned   b. unusual   c. conversational

B. On another piece of paper, write a response to each question. Use the boldface word in your answer and underline the word. Use a dictionary, if necessary.

indictment	1. How did the people feel when the jury charged their civil leader?
invocation	2. What message did the clergy deliver to the world leaders?
epilogue	3. Did you understand the conclusion of that mystery novel?
soliloquy	4. In what kind of situation is Hamlet's "To be or not to be?" quoted?
advocate	5. When would it be important to have someone defend you?

Vocabulary Practice 11: Word Roots

Word Roots: -tain-, -ten-, -tend-, -tens-, -tent-

A **word root** is a word part that forms the basic part of a word. If you know the meaning of a root form, you can determine the meaning of the whole word.

The Latin root -tain- means "hold." The words *retain*, which means "hold back," and *contain*, which means "hold within," have the same root. The roots -ten-, -tend-, -tent-, and -tens- mean "stretch" or "strain."

A. Use the clues to match the boldface word with its definition. Write the letter of the definition before the word. Check your answers in a dictionary.

	Word	Clue	Definition
1. _____	**contain**	liquid	a. to expand, become swollen
2. _____	**tenacious**	child	b. to stretch out
3. _____	**retain**	wall	c. to strain against as in a contest or conflict
4. _____	**tenure**	teacher	d. undergoing tension
5. _____	**portend**	omen	e. to hold back, confine
6. _____	**distend**	river	f. to enclose, hold something within
7. _____	**contend**	boxer	g. to hold or keep in possession
8. _____	**extend**	elastic	h. the right to hold property or a position
9. _____	**detain**	prisoner	i. holding firmly, stubbornly
10. _____	**tensile**	high wire	j. to stretch through, foreshadow

B. Circle the word that best completes each sentence.

1. I fear *contention/extension* with my opponent in the tournament.

2. As the rains continued, the engineers kept close watch over the *distending/retaining* wall.

3. Professor Ansen sighed in relief when the academic committee offered him *containment/tenure.*

4. Kim sat in *detention/retention* during the pep rally for throwing spitballs in class.

5. I promised not to tell, but I just could not *contain/detain* Jilian's secret any longer.

6. The team's star player hoped to *extend/distend* his hitting streak to thirty games.

7. We all worried about the exam, but no one was as *tenacious/tensile* as Sarah.

8. The child's *tenacity/tenure* caused him to spend many afternoons in his room.

9. Eating a whole pizza caused my stomach to *distend/contend* uncomfortably.

10. The clouds *portended/extended* our devastating loss in the game that day.

C. On other paper, write a sentence for the words you did not circle in Exercise B.

Vocabulary Practice 12 : Word Roots

Word Roots: -sphere-, -spir-, -spiro-

A **word root** is a word part that forms the basic part of a word. If you know the meaning of a root form, you can determine the meaning of the whole word.

The Latin root -spir- means "to breathe." The words *inspire*, which means "to breathe life," and *conspire*, which means "to breathe together," have the same root word. The Latin root -sphere- means "ball." The word *hemisphere* means "one-half of a sphere."

A. Write as many words as you can with the root -spir- or -spiro-, which means "to breathe." Add prefixes and suffixes to build words. Use a dictionary, if necessary. Use this list to begin the word web.

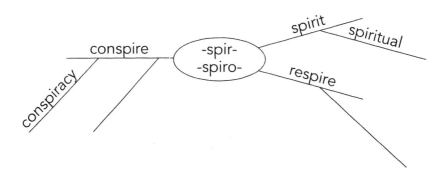

B. Add the root -sphere- to each word part and write the whole word. Write a definition for each word and check it in a dictionary. Add other words with the root -sphere- and their meanings to this list.

1. *atmos-* means "air" _____

2. *eco-* means "house" _____

3. *iono-* means "electrically charged atoms" _____

4. *bio* means "life" _____

5. *bathy* means "deep sea" _____

_____

_____

_____

_____

_____

_____

_____

Vocabulary Practice 13: Word Roots

Word Roots: -luc-, -lum-, -photo-

A **word root** is a word part that forms the basic part of a word. If you know the meaning of a root form, you can determine the meaning of the whole word.

The Latin root -lum- means "light." The words *luminous*, which means "shining," and *illuminating*, which means "giving light," have the same root. The roots -photo- and -luc- also mean "light."

A. Circle the words with a root meaning "light."

1. The translucent ceiling allowed plenty of sunlight to come through.

2. By studying photons in a laboratory, scientists have been able to determine how long it takes light from the sun to reach the Earth.

3. Many people gathered in the park to hear the words of the roaming illuminati.

4. The mountain lake was so pellucid that I could see the plants along the bottom.

5. Our town spared no expense hosting the luminary on her world tour.

6. Ally's photogenic baby girl was in demand for baby supply advertisements.

7. Until my biology teacher explained phototropism, I had no idea why my plants always grew unevenly toward the window.

8. Although suffering injuries, the elderly man was lucid and could explain the accident.

9. I wish the teacher would elucidate the history lessons for some of us.

10. The eerie luminescence of the chemical reaction was brighter than we expected.

B. Write the words you circled beside their definitions.

Root	Word	Definition
1. *-luc-*	_____	clearheaded, rational
2. *-luc-*	_____	letting light pass through
3. *-lum-*	_____	a giving off of light
4. *-photo-*	_____	growth of a plant toward or away from light
5. *-lum-*	_____	person with intellectual or spiritual enlightenment
6. *-luc-*	_____	to make clear
7. *-luc-*	_____	transparent; clear
8. *-photo-*	_____	likely to look good in photographs
9. *-lum-*	_____	object that gives off light; well-known person
10. *-photo-*	_____	particle of light

C. On other paper, write another word with each word root meaning "light."

Vocabulary Practice 14: Synonyms

A **synonym** is a word similar in meaning to another word.

Example: *Distend* is a synonym for *swell*.

A. Write a synonym for each word. Use a dictionary or thesaurus, if necessary.

1. **augment** _____
2. **indulge** _____
3. **cultivate** _____
4. **indignant** _____
5. **stabilize** _____

6. **venture** (n.) _____
7. **dissipate** _____
8. **epitaph** _____
9. **encroach** _____
10. **solidarity** _____

B. Complete the sentences with the boldface words in Exercise A. Then, write a sentence using the synonym for the boldface word.

1. Tightrope walkers hold a heavy pole to help _____ them as they perform.

   _____

2. Speaking through a megaphone will _____ the volume of your voice.

   _____

3. Climbing Mount Everest is a grueling, dangerous _____ .

   _____

4. Weather and time had worn away the _____ on the pioneer's tombstone.

   _____

5. You are bound to gain weight if you _____ every food craving.

   _____

6. The students displayed _____ when presenting their complaints to the

   principal.

   _____

7. Mrs. Jenkins took her daughter to art museums to _____ appreciation of art.

   _____

8. In a small apartment, roommates try not to _____ on each other's privacy.

   _____

9. The new parents watched their savings _____ for the newborn's necessities.

   _____

10. The diplomat was _____ when a party guest mistook him for a waiter.

    _____

Vocabulary Practice 15: Synonyms

A **synonym** is a word similar or exact in meaning to another word.

    Example: *Jubilant* is a synonym for *happy*.

A. Write another synonym for the boldface word.

Word		Synonyms	Word		Synonyms
1. **esoteric**	obscure	_____	6. **sagacious**	wise	_____
2. **felicity**	happiness	_____	7. **unwieldy**	awkward	_____
3. **hindrance**	obstacle	_____	8. **furtive**	secretive	_____
4. **boisterous**	rowdy	_____	9. **moribund**	dying	_____
5. **repugnant**	disgusting	_____	10. **quandary**	predicament	_____

B. Replace each word in italics with a boldface word from Exercise A to make a new phrase. Then, write a sentence using the new phrase.

1. *unruly* party guests _____

_____

2. *wise* elderly man _____

_____

3. bride's *joy* _____

_____

4. *repulsive* odor _____

_____

5. unexpected *barrier* _____

_____

6. *confusing* research paper _____

_____

7. *withering* foliage _____

_____

8. job applicant's *dilemma* _____

_____

9. *sidewise* glances _____

_____

10. *bulky* furniture

_____

C. On other paper, write a sentence using a synonym for each boldface word in Exercise A.

Vocabulary Practice 16: Synonyms

A **synonym** is a word similar or exact in meaning to another word. Synonyms are one kind of word relationship used in analogies. To complete an analogy of synonyms, identify the word pair that are synonyms.

Example: GIGANTIC: HUGE :: MADNESS : INSANITY

A. Choose a synonym from the list to complete the first pair of words in each analogy. Then, circle the letter for the pair of words that completes the analogy.

watch	explain	criminal	restrict	admission
forgive	analyze	agreement	accumulate	serious

1. HOARD:_____ :: _____
   a. convoke: assemble   b. subsequent: first   c. prudent: careless

2. ACCEPTANCE:_____ :: _____
   a. taciturn: still   b. judgmental: illegal   c. obtuse: sharp

3. ACCESS:_____ :: _____
   a. precarious: untruthful   b. prudent: careful   c. convoke: buy

4. OBSERVE:_____ :: _____
   a. judgmental: official   b. impervious: rude   c. taciturn: tight-lipped

5. DISSECT:_____ :: _____
   a. aesthetic: clean   b. subsequent: following   c. precarious: expensive

6. GRAVE:_____ ::_____
   a. impervious: impenetrable   b. convoke: arrest   c. taciturn: impatient

7. SPARE:_____ :: _____
   a. disparage: ridicule   b. convoke: swear   c. obtuse: long

8. INHIBIT:_____ :: _____
   a. impervious : distant   b. subsequent: watery   c. aesthetic: artistic

9. CLARIFY:_____ ::_____
   a. prudent: shy   b. judgmental: critical   c. disparage: throw away

10. OUTLAW:_____ :: _____
    a. subsequent: forbidden   b. precarious: risky   c. impervious: transparent

B. Circle the word to complete the first pair of words in the analogy.

1. confound:(confuse, conform, discover)::pulverize:grind
2. disparage:(elevate, discover, belittle)::prudent:cautious
3. impervious:(unaffected, busy, agitated) ::juvenile:youth
4. precarious:(confident, uncertain, rushed)::judgmental:condemning
5. taciturn:(boisterous, uncommunicative, brave)::obtuse:blunt

C. On other paper, replace one of the synonyms in the second pair of each analogy in Exercise B.

Vocabulary Practice 17: Antonyms

An **antonym** is a word whose meaning is opposite to another word.

Example: *Courageous* is an antonym for *cowardly.*

A. Each sentence has one word that is an antonym for one of the boldface words at the end of the sentence. Find the word in the sentence and circle it. Then, choose the antonym and write it in the sentence. The first one is an example.

1. The amicable politician stood out in contrast to his (aggressive) opponent.

   amicable/assertive

2. Calvin was such a _____ worker that everyone else appeared slovenly by contrast.

   fastidious/sluggish

3. The symposium speaker was _____ and would not even acknowledge her unpretentious colleagues.

   arrogant/humble

4. We were surprised by the _____ donation made by the usually generous mayor.

   charitable/miserly

5. The opposing team's athletes were very _____ in comparison to our in-competent ones.

   adept/incapable

6. Our candidate's _____ nature was threatening to his disingenuous opponent.

   deceitful/candid

7. The teacher's mathematical _____ baffled students until they discovered a solution.

   vita/conundrum

8. After the worst forecast, the weather proved _____ for enjoying the game.

   optimal/horrendous

9. I was surprised that the formerly heavy movie star was _____ in her films.

   slender/sweet

10. My professor thinks I am _____ —never at a loss for words.

   unspecific/prolific

B. Write a sentence about each topic. Use an antonym from Exercise A for each word in italics.

1. the *meek* Hollywood actor _____

2. the community's *solution* _____

3. a tailor who is *unskilled* at sewing _____

4. a *miserly* billionaire _____

5. the *combative* argument _____

Vocabulary Practice 18: Antonyms

An **antonym** is a word whose meaning is opposite to another word.

Example: *Impoverished* is an antonym for *rich*.

A. Choose the boldface word that is the antonym for each set of words. Use a dictionary or the-saurus, if necessary.

sanguine	**mundane**	**expedient**	**neophyte**	**innumerable**
taper	**motley**	**insatiable**	**peevish**	**plausible**

1. impossible, unlikely _____

2. unusual, unique _____

3. fulfilled, content _____

4. few, not many _____

5. pessimistic, hopeless _____

6. agreeable, good-natured _____

7. inconvenient, impractical _____

8. professional, master _____

9. identical, homogenous _____

10. widen, expand _____

B. Choose a boldface word from the list in Exercise A that belongs in each sentence. Then, complete each sentence using an *antonym* for the same word.

1. Traveler's checks are certainly _____ when _____.

2. The movie's plot structure was so _____ that I'll _____

3. You would think my cat is rather _____ judging by _____.

4. Nancy had a _____ expression on her face when _____.

5. Larry made a list of terms to teach the computer _____ because

   _____.

6. My new neighbors are _____ considering all the _____.

7. Murray gave a _____ explanation for how he _____.

8. The river will _____ at the source, but _____.

9. Gazing at the sky as a child, I had no idea the stars were _____ , but

   thought _____.

10. The _____ appearance of the costumed guests was in contrast to

    _____.

Vocabulary Practice 19: Antonyms

An **antonym** is a word whose meaning is opposite to another word.

  Example: *Cruel* is an antonym for *kind.*

A. Read each pair of sentences. Write the antonym in the second sentence for the underlined word or words in the first sentence.

umkempt	innocuous	auspicious	resolute	excessive
destitute	effervescent	insufficient	pliable	sterile

1. Jimmy was indecisive about the flavor of ice cream he wanted.

   Normally, he was _____ about every choice he made.

2. My first semester was discouraging because I didn't study or go to classes.

   My roommate had an _____ beginning to his college career with great grades.

3. The forest rangers are now allowing campfires because we've had abundant rain.

   Earlier this year the ban on campfires was in effect because of the _____ rainfall.

4. People often think they are comfortable financially until it is too late.

   Some people are too proud to get help until they are completely _____

5. At the beginning of the party, everyone was restrained and quiet.

   Thankfully, the host was quite _____ and livened the party.

6. Mom drinks a moderate amount of coffee every day.

   Dad drinks five cups every day, which I think is quite _____.

7. Many types of snakes are harmful even though they appear not to be.

   Though it may look scary, a black snake is actually rather _____.

8. Some rulers are made of rigid material and can be used in limited ways.

   Thinking the measuring stick was _____ , Jaqueline snapped it in half.

9. Johnny's injury to his knee was not cleaned, so it became infected.

   A hospital operating room requires a _____ environment.

10. Jared was a straight A student and was well groomed and polished.

   Although he was a straight A student, Jeremy appeared _____ and

   lackadaisical.

B. Write antonyms for these words that are different from those used in the sentences above. Check your answers in a thesaurus or dictionary.

1. **excessive** _____

2. **effervescent** _____

3. **auspicious** _____

4. **resolute** _____

5. **innocuous** _____

Name _____   Date _____

Vocabulary Practice 20: Synonym and Antonym Review

A. Complete the following synonym and antonym analogies. To determine the analogy relationship, look at the first pair of words. If they are synonyms, choose the pair of words that are synonyms to complete the analogy. If the first pair of words are antonyms, choose the antonym pair to complete the analogy.

1. FASTIDIOUS: TIDY :: INNUMERABLE: _____
   - a. countless
   - b. precocious
   - c. prolific

2. ADEPT: SKILLED :: CONNUNDRUM: _____
   - a. solution
   - b. confusion
   - c. mystery

3. AUGMENT: REDUCE :: BOISTEROUS: _____
   - a. perfect
   - b. repugnant
   - c. taciturn

4. UNKEMPT: MESSY :: ARROGANT: _____
   - a. haughty
   - b. humble
   - c. banal

5. DISPERSE: SUMMON :: PRECARIOUS: _____
   - a. judicious
   - b. insecure
   - c. certain

6. SUBSEQUENT: PRECEDING :: OBTUSE: _____
   - a. dishonest
   - b. sharp
   - c. poignant

7. AESTHETIC: REPUGNANT:: IMPERVIOUS: _____
   - a. beautiful
   - b. necessary
   - c. penetrable

8. PLIABLE: FLEXIBLE:: SVELTE: _____
   - a. important
   - b. slender
   - c. spendthrift

9. CULTIVATE: DESTROY:: ESOTERIC _____
   - a. earthly
   - b. unexciting
   - c. refreshing

10. EFFERVESCENT: LIVELY :: MOTLEY: _____
    - a. conformed
    - b. meandering
    - c. assorted

11. AUSPICIOUS: SANGUINE :: PROLIFIC: _____
    - a. productive
    - b. natural
    - c. destitute

12. UNWIELDY: CONVENIENT :: SAGACIOUS: _____
    - a. foolish
    - b. wise
    - c. uncaring

13. FRIENDLY: AMICABLE :: AMBIVALENT: _____
    - a. optimal
    - b. rational
    - c. indefinite

14. DESTITUTE: IMPOVERISHED :: STERILE: _____
    - a. contaminated
    - b. sanitary
    - c. prolific

15. FELICITY: UNHAPPINESS :: QUANDARY: _____
    - a. solution
    - b. newcomer
    - c. difficulty

B. On another piece of paper, write a new pair of words to complete each analogy.

© Prentice-Hall, Inc.

Vocabulary Practice 21: Analogies

An **analogy** is a relationship between a pair of words. In an analogy, the relationship between the first pair of words is the same as the relationship between the second pair of words.

Example: One type of analogy is a *function* relationship. In EAR : HEAR :: EYE : SEE, *hear* and *see* are functions of ear and eye.

Example: Another type of analogy a *cause-effect* relationship. In BURN : PAIN :: SLEEP : REST, *burn* causes *pain*, and *sleep* causes *rest*.

A. Determine the relationship between the first pair of words. Write the word that completes the analogy.

1. SYNERGY : EFFICIENCY :: EFFORT : _____

   a. trying   b. waste   c. success

2. CLEANSE : STERILIZE :: EULOGY : _____

   a. death   b. honor   c. sharpen

3. BANALITY : APATHY :: READING : _____

   a. completion   b. knowledge   c. texts

4. CARELESSNESS : MISTAKES :: HURRICANE : _____

   a. destruction   b. eye   c. sunshine

5. TENT : COVER :: AIRPLANE : _____

   a. fast   b. sky   c. transport

6. RUDDER : STEER :: ANCHOR : _____

   a. stabilize   b. dissipate   c. loosen

7. SOAP : CLEANLINESS :: CONUNDRUM : _____

   a. confusion   b. understanding   c. motivation

8. ANTICLIMAX : SURPRISE :: COUNTERMEASURE : _____

   a. prevent   b. support   c. weigh

9. PROPELLENT : MOVE :: EDICT : _____

   a. sympathize   b. repel   c. declare

10. EDUCATION : LITERACY :: OVERLOAD : _____

    a. celebration   b. stress   c. laziness

B. Write a word to complete these *function* and *cause-effect* analogies.

1. DISAGREEMENT : STRIFE :: RELAXATION: _____

2. MONARCHY : RULE :: ANTISEPTIC: _____

3. DROUGHT : DEARTH :: ENCOURAGEMENT : _____

4. LAMP : ILLUMINATE :: LAWNMOWER: _____

5. HURDLE : SETBACK :: ACHIEVEMENT : _____

C. On other paper, write a *cause-effect* and a *function* analogy and label them.

Vocabulary Practice 22: Analogies

An **analogy** is a relationship between a pair of words. In an analogy, the relationship between the first pair of words is the same as the relationship between the second pair of words.

Example: One type of analogy expresses a *part to whole* relationship.
In WOLF : PACK :: COW : HERD, *wolf* is part of *pack*, and *cow* is part of *herd*.

Example: Another type of analogy shows a "type of" or "part of" relationship.
In NEON : GAS :: QUARTZ : MINERAL, *neon* is a type of *gas*, and *quartz* is a type of *mineral*.

A. Complete the following *part to whole* and *type of* analogies.

1. INDIVIDUAL : COMMUNITY :: SENATOR : _____
   a. law   b. capitol   c. congress

2. BASEBALL : SPORT :: JOGGING : _____
   a. cardiovascular   b. sprinting   c. exercise

3. ZENITH : MOUNTAIN :: STEP : _____
   a. rail   b. escalator   c. elevator

4. PAGE : BOOK :: FLOUR : _____
   a. cake   b. baking   c. unbleached

5. PORCELAIN : CLAY :: SPANISH : _____
   a. language   b. vacation   c. city

6. STALK : CORNFIELD :: FISH : _____
   a. mammal   b. trout   c. school

7. EXHAUST : POLLUTION :: LIMERICK : _____
   a. book   b. person   c. poem

8. BUS : VEHICLE :: RAIN : _____
   a. snow   b. weather   c. lake

9. MOUNTAIN : RANGE :: BRICK : _____
   a. architecture   b. mason   c. wall

10. BEEHIVE : HAIRSTYLE :: FAX : _____
   a. communication   b. telephone   c. e-mail

B. Write a word to complete each analogy: "function," part-to-whole," or "type of."

1. thermos : insulate :: paperclip _____

2. latex : paint :: potassium : _____

3. island : archipelago :: captain : _____

4. aridity : thirst :: stretching : _____

5. granite : rock :: mahogany : _____

C. Beside each analogy in Exercise A and B, write the type of analogy given.

Vocabulary Practice 23: Analogies

An **analogy** is a relationship between a pair of words. Analogies show relationships between two pairs of words.

A. You have studied several types of analogies: *synonyms, antonyms, function, cause-effect, part to whole,* and *type of* relationships. Determine the relationship in the first pair of words. Then, choose the word that completes the analogy.

1. SCHOONER : SHIP :: NOVEL: _____
   - a. mystery
   - b. fiction
   - c. romance

2. FELICITY : JOY :: OBTUSE: _____
   - a. poignant
   - b. triangle
   - c. blunt

3. RADISH : VEGETABLE :: LEMON: _____
   - a. juice
   - b. yellow
   - c. fruit

4. OVERWORK : EXHAUSTION :: EXPEDIENCY : _____
   - a. savings
   - b. waste
   - c. confusion

5. ASTUTE : IGNORANT :: AUGMENT : _____
   - a. reimburse
   - b. grow
   - c. diminish

6. FASTIDIOUS : ORGANIZED :: NEOPHYTE : _____
   - a. master
   - b. novice
   - c. nymph

7. LANGUAGE : COMMUNICATION :: CLOTHING : _____
   - a. warmth
   - b. variety
   - c. colors

8. KITCHEN : HOUSE :: LUNG : _____
   - a. breathe
   - b. oxygen
   - c. torso

9. DISTEND : COMPRESS :: MALEVOLENT : _____
   - a. kind
   - b. selfish
   - c. evil

10. CONNUNDRUM : PERPLEX :: ANTISEPTIC : _____
    - a. lotion
    - b. infection
    - c. disinfect

B. Choose the word pair that completes the following analogies.

1. BOISTEROUS : CLAMOROUS :: _____
   - a. anger: emotion
   - b. infallible: imperfect
   - c. walking: endurance

2. FRICTION : HEAT :: _____
   - a. oil: slick
   - b. moisture: dampness
   - c. politics: government

3. VACCINE : IMMUNIZE :: _____
   - a. dictum: instruct
   - b. slow: prudent
   - c. doctor: profession

4. KNOTTY : SMOOTH :: _____
   - a. rope: climb
   - b. conform: authority
   - c. depressed: elated

5. GENERAL : ARMY :: _____
   - a. conflict: devastation
   - b. member: committee
   - c. cook: chef

C. Beside each analogy in Exercises A and B, write the type of analogy given.

Name _____ Date _____

Vocabulary Practice 24: Connotations and Denotations

A **connotation** is the implied or suggested meaning of a word or phrase. A **denotation** is the dictionary definition of a word. Words with similar meanings convey different connotations, depending on the text.

Example: *Welcome* and *accost* have the same denotative meaning, "to greet." *Welcome* has a positive connotation, meaning "greet favorably," while *accost* has a negative connotation, meaning "greet in a challenging way."

A. Use a dictionary to write the denotation for each word.

1. contrite _____

2. cowardly _____

3. ornate _____

4. strife _____

5. vacillate _____

6. recant _____

7. lassitude _____

8. opulent _____

9. melancholy _____

10. plaintive _____

B. For each boldface word, write two words from the list that convey similar meanings, but different connotations.

afraid	repudiate	falter	apathy	weariness
affluent	spineless	hesitate	despair	magnificent
gaudy	moodiness	decorated	warfare	mournful
retract	humbled	unrest	disconsolate	penitent

1. **recant** _____ _____   6. **ornate** _____ _____

2. **cowardly** _____ _____   7. **strife** _____ _____

3. **vacillate** _____ _____   8. **plaintive** _____ _____

4. **contrite** _____ _____   9. **opulent** _____ _____

5. **melancholy** _____ _____   10. **lassitude** _____ _____

C. On other paper, write a sentence with one of the connotations for each boldface word in Exercise B.

Vocabulary Practice 25: Connotations and Denotations

A **connotation** is the implied or suggested meaning of a word or phrase. A **denotation** is the dictionary definition of a word. Words with similar meanings convey different connotations, depending on the context.

Example: The words *dinner*, *feast*, and *banquet* have meanings related to eating or dining. Each word, however, conveys a different connotation, or implied meaning.

A. For each sentence, write the boldface word that conveys the appropriate connotation.

1. **barren** and **commonplace**

    a. The new director's play was completely _____ and devoid of creativity.

    b. Joan thought her apartment was exciting, but her friend thought it was _____.

2. **soothe** and **conciliate**

    a. A soft lullaby was enough to _____ the baby and stop her crying fit.

    b. European nations tried many times to _____ the Germans before WWII.

3. **raucous** and **earsplitting**

    a. The jet plane noise was so _____ that it frightened all the passengers.

    b. All the band members were novices, and their first CD was quite _____.

4. **playful** and **degenerate**

    a. The little puppy gave its owner a _____ bite on the ankles.

    b. Some _____ students painted our football field before the big game.

5. **contrived** and **fabricated**

    a. Everyone believed that Ed's story was _____ to keep him out of trouble.

    b. The highway interchange was _____ with the best materials available.

6. **imitate** and **rival**

    a. Martin Luther King, Jr., would be a good civil leader to _____.

    b. Only Michelle can _____ Tara for the class presidency.

7. **uncover** and **betray**

    a. Scientists hope one day to _____ the answers to the lost city of Arum.

    b. The prosecutor's cross-examination forced Ally to _____ her secret.

8. **leniency** and **negligence**

    a. Sue's _____ in caring for her vegetable garden resulted in a loss of produce.

    b. Aaron is a spoiled adult because of his parents' _____ with him as a child.

9. **penetrating** and **acute**

    a. The coach had a(n) _____ ability to predict the other team's strategy.

    b. Drew's shoulder pain was more _____ than he had ever experienced after a game.

10. **tenacious** and **continuous**

    a. Willa was so _____ with her opinion that it was pointless to argue.

    b. The rain was _____ for several weeks, spoiling everyone's vacation plans.

B. On other paper, write two more words that are connotations for each boldface word in Exercise A.

Name _____ Date _____

Vocabulary Practice: 26: Connotations and Denotations

A **connotation** is the implied or suggested meaning of a word or phrase. A **denotation** is the dictionary definition of a word. A word may have many connotations suggesting positive, negative, or neutral feelings, depending on the text.

Example: Connotations of *humble* include *bashful, fearful, modest,* and *shy* among other words. The choice of a word in a sentence conveys the connotation.

A. Complete each sentence with a word from the list to convey the connotation of the word *humble.* You may use some words more than once. Use a dictionary or thesaurus, as necessary.

apprehensive, bashful, blushing, courteous, deferential, demure, docile, fearful, gentle, hesitant, meek, mild, modest, obliging, polite, quiet, reserved, respectful, sedate, shy, soft-spoken, submissive, timid, unassuming, withdrawn

1. While Ike's enormous hands look like they could crush stone, he was surprisingly

   _____ when it came to holding the kittens.

2. When answering questions from adults, the _____ boy showed that

   his parents had taught him manners.

3. Rather than take initiative, the _____ waiter wouldn't leave the

   kitchen until the chef told him to.

4. Jessica was so _____ during dinner that everyone forgot she was at the table.

5. Although the supervisor was _____, everyone followed her orders as

   quickly as possible.

6. If you're going to play linebacker in college, there's no point in being _____.

7. Andy's demeanor is so _____ that he never offends anyone.

8. There is a time to be _____ and a time to take action.

9. Steve wanted to be _____ during his job interview, but the inter-

   viewer just said he had no legs to stand on.

10. Alice bought a basset hound because she wanted a _____ dog, but

    she never expected it to sleep all day!

11. The other team's smallest player proved to be anything but _____.

12. After many years of being _____, David finally overcame the lack of

    confidence he had in middle school.

13. When traveling to other countries, a _____ attitude will often go

    much further than words.

14. Seeing Anthony on stage, no one believed that he is normally a _____ person.

15. One of the first skills taught in a self-defense class is to walk in a way that is not

    _____.

B. Choose one of the sentences in Exercise A to begin a paragraph. On other paper, add two or three sentences, using words from the list in Exercise A. Include details or other information to convey the appropriate connotations of the words used.

Vocabulary Practice 27: Commonly Misused Words

Several words in English are pronounced the same, but have different meanings and spellings, causing confusion. These words are **homonyms.**

Example: *Blue* and *blew* are homonyms.

A. Write the definitions of each set of homonyms, using the dictionary, if necessary.

1. rein, reign, rain _____

_____

2. discreet, discrete _____

_____

3. stationery, stationary _____

_____

4. compliment, complement _____

_____

5. waiver, waver _____

_____

6. straight, strait _____

_____

7. root, route _____

_____

8. site, sight, cite _____

_____

9. capital, capitol _____

_____

10. aid, aide _____

_____

B. Write the word from Exercise A that best completes each sentence.

1. The accountant made a _____ inquiry into the family finances.

2. Tim's tie seems to _____ his suit perfectly.

3. Unless he is usurped, a king's _____ lasts his lifetime.

4. Each student needs a signed _____ from parents to take the field trip.

5. Engineers have already begun to plan the _____ for the new city park.

C. On other paper, write a sentence for each word in Exercise A that you did not use in Exercise B.

Vocabulary Practice 28: Commonly Misused Words

Many English words and phrases are confused because they sound similar or their meanings are not understood.

Example: *Persevere* and *endure* both mean "to continue." *Persevere* means "to persist regardless of opposition," while *endure* means "to hold up under difficulty" or "to remain."

A. Write the pairs of words next to their definitions. Use a dictionary, if necessary.

proved/proven	ceremonial/ceremonious	aural/oral
aggravate/irritate	assume/presume	

1. _____ : v. to take on the role or appearance; take upon oneself; take for granted

   _____ : v. to take upon oneself without permission or authority; deduce; suppose

2. _____ : adj. known to be valid, effective, or genuine

   _____ : v. to be found or shown by experience or trial; to turn out to be

3. _____ : n. a rite or ritual

   _____ : adj. full of ceremony; characterized by formality; excessively proper

4. _____ : v. to make worse; to make more burdensome or troublesome

   _____ : v. to excite; to anger, provoke, annoy

5. _____ : adj. related to the ear or hearing

   _____ : adj. uttered from the mouth; related to speech or speaking

B. Complete the sentences with the boldface words you wrote in Exercise A. Some words require suffixes. The numbered pairs correspond to the numbered pairs of definitions.

1. a. With her father in the hospital, Sue has _____ the household chores.

   b. Students who _____ to know more than the biology teacher changed their minds.

2. a. The detective who had a hunch about the case later _____ to be right.

   b. While health claims come and go, orange juice is a _____ source of vitamin C.

3. a. The banquet was interesting, but too _____ for elementary children.

   b. The village's _____ to celebrate the harvest lasted for more than two weeks.

4. a. Each time the striking workers reach a tentative agreement, something _____ the situation.

   b. Wanting to play, the young child continued to _____ the sleeping dog.

5. a. Cultures that do not have a written language rely on _____ tradition to communicate history and tradition to each generation.

   b. People who lose their sense of sight develop stronger _____ perceptions.

C. On another piece of paper, write the definitions and a sentence for each of these word pairs: *allusion/illusion; quote/quotation.*

Name _____ Date _____

Vocabulary Practice 29: Commonly Misused Words

Many English words and phrases sound alike and cause confusion when not used correctly.

Example: The words *devise* and *device* look and sound similar, but have different meanings. *Devise* is a verb meaning "to think up or invent something," while *device* is a noun meaning "something created."

A. Using the definitions, write each numbered pair of words in the corresponding numbered sentences. Some words require suffixes.

1. devise: to think up or invent something
2. *older:* from an earlier period of time
3. *differ from:* to be dissimilar
4. *preclude:* to stop in advance
5. *loath:* unwilling, reluctant
6. *uninterested:* indifferent, not interested
7. *compare to:* similar items
8. *emigrate:* to leave a country or region
9. *raise:* to cause to move higher or increase
10. *cynical:* critical of others' lives, sarcastic

1. device: something created
2. *elder:* a person who is old
3. *differ with:* to disagree with
4. *prevent:* to keep from happening
5. *loathe:* to dislike greatly
6. *disinterested:* lack of bias toward
7. *compare with:* differences
8. *immigrate:* to come into a new place
9. *raze:* to grow, increase, move vertically
10. *skeptical:* doubting, questioning

1. Jonas knew the old captain was wrong, but he was _____ to speak out
   against his _____.

2. The carpenter wanted to _____ the kitchen ceiling, but the homeowner
   was _____ in the idea.

3. No state of the art weather _____ can _____ hurricanes
   from occurring.

4. People _____ from foreign countries to the United States; many countries
   are _____ the United States in raising the quotas for immigrants.

5. Lauren _____ the color green, a fact that _____ her from
   being a successful landscape painter.

6. Mark was _____ about Sarah's new business venture, and he made very
   _____ remarks.

7. The populations in the coastal cities have been _____ steadily ever since
   the governor loosened the requirements to _____.

8. Senators Jollis and Mayfield _____ each other so much that it is difficult
   to believe they will ever _____ a solution to the budget problem.

9. One way Indian and African elephants _____ each other is that the African
   elephant can live to be much _____ that its Indian counterpart.

10. _____ similar birds, the jay is completely _____ in any
    attempts to hand-feed it.

B. On another piece of paper, write a paragraph using five words from Exercise A. Use one of the sentences in Exercise A as your topic sentence.

Vocabulary Practice 30: Specialized Vocabulary

While most of the words we use today have their origins in Old English, Greek, and Latin, many words from other languages have been incorporated into English.

A. Match each word with its definition by writing the letter of the definition before the word. Use a dictionary, if necessary. Then, refer to the dictionary to write the language of origin after each word.

Word and Language of Origin

			Definition
1.	_____ albatross	_____	a. person of great learning
2.	_____ ballast	_____	b. small fleet of boats
3.	_____ pagoda	_____	c. Latin American rhythm instrument
4.	_____ syllabus	_____	d. object thought to contain magic power
5.	_____ foist	_____	e. social blunder; lack of tact
6.	_____ azure	_____	f. large room used for receptions
7.	_____ talisman	_____	g. long, narrow boat
8.	_____ papyrus	_____	h. to push about; to move hurriedly
9.	_____ pundit	_____	i. large, web-footed bird
10.	_____ gondola	_____	j. summary or outline
11.	_____ guiro	_____	k. loosely fitting clothing
12.	_____ flotilla	_____	l. complete defeat, frustration
13.	_____ algebra	_____	m. hot spring that gushes steam and water
14.	_____ etch	_____	n. tall water plant abundant in the Nile region
15.	_____ faux pas	_____	o. mathematical system using symbols
16.	_____ pajamas	_____	p. several story pyramidal temple
17.	_____ hustle	_____	q. to make a drawing on metal or glass using acid
18.	_____ geyser	_____	r. to get something sold or accepted by deception
19.	_____ checkmate	_____	s. anything heavy used to provide stability
20.	_____ saloon	_____	t. sky blue

B. Use a dictionary to find five additional words that have origins in languages other than Old English, Greek, and Latin. Write the words and their definitions. Explain how their original meanings may have led to their current definitions.

_____

_____

_____

_____

_____

_____

Vocabulary Practice 31: Specialized Vocabulary

Many English words are specific to occupations, professions, or vocations. Having a basic understanding of legal and medical terms is useful in daily life.

A. Use a dictionary to write definitions for this list of medical and legal terms.

aneurysm	antibiotic	appellate court	assault	clinic
deposition	histology	internist	larceny	libel
misdemeanor	ophthalmologist	paralysis	plagiarism	specialist

1. _____

2. _____

3. _____

4. _____

5. _____

6. _____

7. _____

8. _____

9. _____

10. _____

11. _____

12. _____

13. _____

14. _____

15. _____

B. Organize the words in Exercise A under the headings shown.

Medical   **Legal**

_____   _____   _____   _____

_____   _____   _____   _____

_____   _____   _____   _____

_____   _____   _____   _____

C. Look at a newspaper, magazine, legal or medical document, or other source for an example of how each word or phrase in Exercise B is used. Gather the examples or copy them, with a reference to the source. Put together a one-page dictionary with the definitions and examples.

Spelling Practice 1: Words With *ei* and *ie*

Words with *ie* and *ei* follow spelling rules with some exceptions.

Spelling Rule: Use *i* before *e* except after *c* or when sounded like *a* as in *neighbor* and *weigh*.

> **Examples:** The word *believe* and others follow the "i before e" rule; the word *receipt* is an example of "except after c." Words such as *height* are exceptions and must be learned. The spelling rule applies only when *ie* or *ei* are in the same syllable. Thus words such as *be' ing* do not follow the rule.

A. Determine whether or not each word is spelled correctly. Write the words that are spelled correctly under the headings that apply for spelling the words. Then, write the misspelled words correctly under the headings. Check your spelling in a dictionary.

peirce	decieve	hienous	beseige	proficeint
freight	counterfiet	percieve	greivous	reciept
inviegh	weird	achieve	reign	cheiftain
consceince	wieght	liesure	concievable	hieress
neither	relieve	efficeint	conceit	mischeivous

i before *e*	Except after *c*	Sounds like *a*	Exception
_____	_____	_____	_____
_____	_____	_____	_____
_____	_____	_____	_____
_____	_____	_____	_____
_____	_____	_____	_____
_____	_____	_____	_____
_____	_____	_____	_____
_____	_____	_____	_____

B. Use the words from Exercise A to complete the following sentences.

1. Although Bill disagreed with the article, he did not need to _____ against the author.

2. Surgeons need to be highly _____ in their respective areas.

3. Ed sustained a very _____ injury from the accident

4. At the turn of the century, it was not _____ that people would go to the moon.

5. There is a fine line between being _____ and being disobedient.

6. A book's antagonist is often an abhorrent and _____ figure.

7. The printer received a ten-year sentence for creating _____ money.

8. Our dog has a hearing problem, but she can _____ distant footsteps.

9. In the middle ages, armies would _____ entire towns, cutting off their supplies.

10. The boy's _____ drove him to return the stolen candy.

Spelling Practice 2: Final e With Suffixes

When spelling words with final *e* and adding suffixes, follow rules for keeping or dropping the silent *e*.

Spelling Rules

1. Drop the final *e* before adding a suffix that begins with a vowel.

Examples: Adding *–est* or *-ing* to *close* makes *closest* and *closing*.

2. Keep the final *e* before adding a suffix that begins with a consonant.

Examples: Adding *-ful* to *grace* makes *graceful*. Adding *-ly* to *large* makes *largely*.

3. Drop the final *e* when adding *-ment* to words ending in *–dge*, but not in most other words that end in *e*.

Examples: Adding *-ment* to *judge* makes *judgment*. Adding *-ment* to *case* makes *casement*.

4. Keep the final *e* when adding *-able* or *-ous* to words ending in *-ce* or *-ge*. In most other words, drop final *e* when adding *able*.

Examples: Adding *-able* to *change* makes *changeable*. Adding *-able* to *move* makes *movable*.

A. Add the suffix to each word, using the spelling rules, and write the new word.

1. *introspective* and *-ly* _____
2. *pore* and *-ous* _____
3. *envelope* and *-ing* _____
4. *console* and *-able* _____
5. *forebode* and *-ing* _____
6. *discourage* and *-ment* _____
7. *obtuse* and *-ly* _____
8. *peace* and *-ful* _____
9. *manage* and *-able* _____
10. *furtive* and *-ly* _____

11. *acknowledge* and *-ment* _____
12. *adventure* and *-ous* _____
13. *salvage* and *-able* _____
14. *engage* and *-ment* _____
15. *interlope* and *-ing* _____
16. *coarse* and *-est* _____
17. *dredge* and *-ing* _____
18. *infringe* and *-ment* _____
19. *rare* and *-est* _____
20. *taste* and *-ful* _____

B. Write each word correctly and write the number of the rule that applies to the spelling when adding a suffix.

1. immeasureable _____ _____
2. arguement _____ _____
3. grudgeing _____ _____
4. perpetuateing _____ _____
5. gracful _____ _____
6. spareest _____ _____
7. outragous _____ _____
8. doteing _____ _____
9. valueable _____ _____
10. sedatly _____ _____

Spelling Practice 3: Final y With Suffixes

When spelling words with final *y* and adding suffixes, follow rules for keeping *y* or changing *y* to *i* before adding the suffix.

Spelling Rules

1. Change *y* to *i* in words ending with a consonant plus *y* before adding suffixes -*ness*, -*er*, -*ed*, -*ly*, and -*ous*.

Example: Adding -*ness* to *hazy* makes *haziness*.

2. Change *y* to *i* before adding suffixes -*ance*, -*ant*, and -*able*.

Example: Adding -*ance* to *apply* makes *appliance*.

3. Keep the final *y* in words ending with a vowel plus *y* before suffixes -*er*, -*ous*, -*ance*, -*ing*, -*ful*, and -*ness*.

Example: Adding -*er* to *buy* makes *buyer*.

4. Keep the final *y* when adding the suffixes -*ing* or -*ish* to avoid having two *i*'s.

Example: Adding -*ing* to *try* makes *trying*.

A. Add the suffixes to the words and write the new words. Check your spelling in a dictionary.

1. *simplify* and -*ing* _____
2. *melody* and -*ous* _____
3. *annoy* and -*ance* _____
4. *hardy* and -*ly* _____
5. *dizzy* and -*ness* _____
6. *coy* and -*ness* _____
7. *unify* and -*er* _____
8. *rely* and -*ant* _____
9. *defray* and -*ing* _____
10. *tardy* and -*ness* _____
11. *justify* and -*able* _____
12. *betray* and -*er* _____
13. *accompany* and -*ing* _____
14. *satisfactory* and -*ly* _____
15. *messy* and -*ness* _____

16. *pity* and -*ed* _____
17. *vary* and -*ant* _____
18. *joy* and -*ous* _____
19. *fortify* and -*able* _____
20. *glory* and -*ous* _____
21. *defy* and -*ance* _____
22. *bounty* and -*ful* _____
23. *baby* and -*ish* _____
24. *obey* and -*ing* _____
25. *employ* and -*er* _____
26. *solidify* and -*ing* _____
27. *duty* and -*ful* _____
28. *signify* and -*ed* _____
29. *haughty* and -*ness* _____
30. *cheery* and -*ly* _____

B. Categorize the words you wrote in Exercise A according to the spelling rule that applies for adding suffixes. You will need an extra piece of paper.

Change y to i

_____

_____

_____

_____

Retain y

_____

_____

_____

_____

Spelling Practice 4: Double the Final Consonant

When adding suffixes to words with a final consonant, follow the spelling rules for doubling the final consonant.

1. Double the final consonant in words ending in a consonant-vowel-consonant (c-v-c) pattern as follows:

a. if the c-v-c syllable is stressed

Example: Adding *-er* to *begin* makes *beginner*.

b. not in an *unstressed* final syllable

Example: Adding *-ed* to *benefit* makes *benefited* (unstressed final syllable).

c. in words ending *fer* when adding *-ed, -er,* or *-ing*

Example: Adding *-ing* to *refer* makes *referring*.

2. Double the final consonant in words ending in two vowels and one consonant when adding a suffix beginning with the *same* final consonant, but not when adding a suffix beginning with a vowel or a different consonant.

Examples: Adding *-ly* to *cool* makes *coolly*. Adding *-able* to *bear* makes *bearable*.

3. Double the final consonant in a one syllable word when adding the suffix *y* or a suffix beginning with a vowel. The letters *w, x,* and *y* are never doubled.

Examples: Adding *-y* to *fog* makes *foggy*. Adding *-ed* to *rub* makes *rubbed*.

4. Do not double the final consonant in words ending in two consonants.

Examples: Adding *-ed* to *pound* makes *pounded*. Adding *-ly* to *calm* makes *calmly*.

5. Do not double the final consonant in words ending in two vowels and a consonant when adding a suffix beginning with a vowel.

Examples: Adding *-able* to *bear* makes *bearable*.

A. Add the suffixes to the words and write the new words

1. *rebel* and *-ed* _____
2. *commit* and *-ment* _____
3. *monogram* and *-ing* _____
4. *occur* and *-ing* _____
5. *casual* and *-ly* _____
6. *benefit* and *-ed* _____
7. *retract* and *-able* _____
8. *tranquil* and *-ly* _____
9. *disappoint* and *-ment* _____
10. *prefer* and *-able* _____
11. *contain* and *-er* _____
12. *program* and *-ed* _____
13. *discover* and *-y* _____
14. *kidnap* and *-er* _____
15. *keen* and *-ness* _____
16. *preen* and *-ing* _____
17. *grip* and *-ed* _____
18. *maneuver* and *-able* _____
19. *wallow* and *-ing* _____
20. *outfit* and *-ed* _____
21. *legal* and *-ly* _____
22. *confer* and *-ed* _____
23. *compat* and *-ible* _____
24. *diagram* and *-ing* _____
25. *regret* and *-able* _____
26. *maintain* and *-ing* _____
27. *disband* and *-ed* _____
28. *taut* and *-ness* _____
29. *plain* and *-ly* _____
30. *defer* and *-ed* _____

Spelling Practice 4: Double the Final Consonant

B. Organize the words in Exercise A under each spelling rule heading for words with a final consonant.

Rule 1	Rule 2	Rule 3	Rule 4
_____	_____	_____	_____
_____	_____	_____	_____
_____	_____	_____	_____
_____	_____	_____	_____
_____	_____	_____	_____
_____	_____	_____	_____
_____	_____	_____	_____
_____	_____	_____	_____
_____	_____	_____	_____
_____	_____	_____	_____
_____	_____	_____	_____
_____	_____	_____	_____
_____	_____	_____	_____
_____	_____	_____	_____
_____	_____	_____	_____
_____	_____	_____	_____
_____	_____	_____	_____
_____	_____	_____	_____

C. Add ten words to each spelling rule for doubling the final consonant.

Rule 1	Rule 2	Rule 3	Rule 4
_____	_____	_____	_____
_____	_____	_____	_____
_____	_____	_____	_____
_____	_____	_____	_____
_____	_____	_____	_____
_____	_____	_____	_____
_____	_____	_____	_____
_____	_____	_____	_____
_____	_____	_____	_____
_____	_____	_____	_____

Spelling Practice 5: Words Ending in *-al*, *-cal*, and *-cle*

Words ending in *-al*, *-cal*, and *-cle* sound alike and are frequently misspelled. The endings *-al*, *-cal*, and *-cle* change words from verbs to nouns and nouns to verbs, adjectives, and other nouns. Follow the rules for spelling words with these endings.

Spelling Rules

1. Adding *-al* to many words does not change the ending unless the word ends in *e*.

Examples: Adding *-al* to *accident* (a noun) makes *accidental* (an adjective). Adding *-al* to *use* (a noun or a verb) makes *usual* (an adjective).

2. When adding *-al* to a word ending in *-y*, the *y* usually changes to *i*.

Example: Adding *-al* to *bury* (a verb) makes *burial* (a noun).

3. The ending *-cal* is usually an adjective ending. The ending *-cle* is usually a noun ending. The *e* at the end of words is changed to *i* or *u* before adding *-cle*.

Examples: Adding *-cal* to *theatre* (a noun) makes *theatrical* (an adjective). Adding *-cle* to *ice* (a noun) makes *icicle* (a noun).

A. Add the endings to the words using the spelling rules. Write the number of the spelling rule that applies.

-cal or -cle

1. chemi _____
2. chroni _____
3. practi _____
4. economi _____
5. mono _____

6. parti _____
7. cubi _____
8. comi _____
9. whimsi _____
10. radi _____

-al

1. ceremony _____
2. sense _____
3. testimony _____
4. deny _____
5. dismiss _____

6. occasion _____
7. race _____
8. industry _____
9. exception _____
10. education _____

B. Complete the sentences with the new words in Exercise A.

1. The school district ordered new _____ materials that placed greater emphasis on computer-assisted teaching.

2. As we drove through the countryside, Grandpa told us _____ stories of life in the early 1900s.

3. The economist is working to find a _____ solution to the state's budget problems.

4. Except for a(n) _____ candy bar, James eats only healthful foods.

5. A _____ for the new product was endorsed by consumers.

C. On other paper, write five words that follow each spelling rule for words with endings *-al*, *-cal*, and *-cle*.

Name _____ Date _____

Spelling Practice 6: Words Ending in -cy and -sy

Words that end in -cy and -sy sound alike and are often misspelled. Some words follow spelling rules. Other words must be remembered.

Spelling Rules

1. The suffix -cy means "condition" or "state." When -cy is added to a word ending in -t, or te, the t or te is usually dropped.

    Example: Adding -cy to *agent* makes *agency*.

    Exception: Adding -cy to *bankrupt* makes *bankruptcy*.

2. The ending -sy is an ending of some nouns.

    Examples: *controversy* and *biopsy*

A. Add the suffix -cy to each word and write the new word. Check your spelling in a dictionary.

1. deficient _____

2. autocrat _____

3. immediate _____

4. dependent _____

5. efficient _____

6. prophet _____

7. competent _____

8. intimate _____

9. transcendent _____

10. delinquent _____

11. adequate _____

12. relevant _____

13. delicate _____

14. buoyant _____

15. truant _____

B. Put a check (√) next to the words spelled correctly. Rewrite the misspelled words correctly. Check your spelling in a dictionary.

1. ecstacy _____   9. fantacy _____

2. bureaucrasy _____   10. intricasy _____

3. frequency _____   11. autopsy _____

4. tendensy _____   12. discrepansy _____

5. embasy _____   13. advocasy _____

6. candidasy _____   14. obstinasy _____

7. accuracy _____   15. courtesy _____

8. hypocricy _____

    © Prentice-Hall, Inc.

Spelling Practice 7: Words Ending in *-ance, -ence, -ant,* and *-ent*

The suffixes *-ance* and *-ence*, meaning "state or condition," and the suffixes *-ant* and *-ent*, meaning "performing or causing," are often misspelled or not used correctly. Words that take the suffix *-ance* also take *-ant* and words that take *-ence* also take *-ent*. When adding these suffixes to words ending in *y*, change the *y* to *i*.

Example: adding *-ance* or *-ant* to *comply* makes *compliance* and *compliant*.

A. Add the suffixes *-ance, -ence, -ant,* or *-ent* to the words and write the new words under the boldface headings. Most words will be used with two endings. The first one is an example.

rely	correspond	differ	attend	maintain
revere	insist	defy	acquaint	reside
acquiesce	reminisce	infer	vigil	indulge

-ance	***-ant***	***-ence***	***-ent***
reliance	reliant	_____	_____
_____	_____	_____	_____
_____	_____	_____	_____
_____	_____	_____	_____
_____	_____	_____	_____
_____	_____	_____	_____
_____	_____	_____	_____
_____	_____	_____	_____
_____	_____	_____	_____

B. Determine whether or not each word is spelled correctly. Put a check (√) beside the words spelled correctly. Write the misspelled words correctly.

1. acquaintence _____
2. tolerent _____
3. opulent _____
4. reluctent _____
5. permanance _____
6. patiance _____
7. corpulant _____
8. complience _____

9. ordinence _____
10. elegant _____
11. translucant _____
12. magnificant _____
13. conductence _____
14. resplendant _____
15. independant _____
16. brilliance _____

Spelling Practice 7: Words Ending in -ance, -ence, -ant, and -ent

17. indignent _____

18. pertinant _____

19. insolance _____

20. ambience _____

21. ascendence _____

22. malevolant _____

23. attendence _____

24. superintendant _____

25. transcendance _____

26. impatiant _____

27. determinent _____

28. condescendence _____

29. prescance _____

30. dissonent _____

C. Complete the sentences with correctly spelled words from Exercise B.

1. The police _____ forbids driving down Main Street on Saturdays.

2. Some musical composers use _____ sounds to create tension in their songs.

3. While some people are able to wait in long lines, others are _____.

4. Tony was astounded by the _____ of Niagara Falls.

5. The school district _____ conducted classroom observations for several days.

6. A material's _____ determines whether it is used as a wire or an insulator.

7. In tuxedos and formal dresses, the senior class looked _____.

8. _____ in a restaurant adds pleasure to the dining experience.

9. Susan won the perfect _____ award for never missing a day of school.

10. After quitting his diet plan again, the man promised complete _____ with the doctor's orders.

11. The water in the Caribbean was so _____ that Sean could see the bottom.

12. Some people believe that the _____ of certain values allows them to apply to more than one culture.

13. The lecturer's _____ excited everyone in the audience.

14. _____ fireworks on July 4th brings thousands of visitors to our city.

15. Smallville's _____ newspaper covered only that town's events.

Spelling Practice 8: Commonly Misspelled Words

Words with double medial consonants are frequently misspelled. Since there are no spelling rules for spelling these words, they must be learned.

A. Underline the misspelled words and write them correctly after the sentences. There are one or more misspelled words in each sentence.

1. Unfortunately, the celar is accesible only from the exterior of the mansion.

   _____

2. The jury found the defendant inocent of all acusations. _____

3. As a source of energy, nuclear fision can be very eficient. _____

4. The chassis of the all-terain vehicle was badly damaged after crossing the gulch.

   _____

5. After glancing over the biology curiculum, Mark wondered if he would complete the courses sucessfully. _____

6. Extensive analyses of octopuses show them to be animals of high inteligence.

   _____

7. Dr. Holbrith gave the initial apearance of being an average profesor, but after his first year of teaching, everyone knew he was briliant. _____

8. Although it is not neccesary to change a car's oil frequently, waiting too long can cause ireparable damage. _____

9. Occassionally, companies give promotions to employees who are not in line for promotion.

   _____

10. After recovering from the embarassment of forgeting his lines, Michael put on a stelar performance. _____

11. Ideally, a traveling salesman has suficient time at home between trips.

    _____

12. The discovery of penicilin and the development of vacines have increased the standard of life all over the world.

13. Although her paper was gramatically correct, Mia's premise was fundamentaly untrue.

    _____

14. The mule's owner had no choice but to supress his frustration over his animal's stuborness.

    _____

15. Tommorow, Lois will have the privillege of a taking private piano lesson from the symphony's pianist. _____

B. List all the words in Exercise A that you rewrote correctly. Underline all the double medial consonants.

_____

_____

_____

_____

_____

Spelling Practice 9: Commonly Misspelled Words

Words with *ei* or *ie* are often misspelled. Apply the rule for spelling words with *ei* or *ie*, which is *i* before *e* except after *c* or when sounded like a as in *neighbor* and *weigh*.

Examples: The words *wield*, *ceiling*, and *weigh* each follow a part of the rule. The spelling of exceptions such as *ancient* and *height* must be memorized.

A. Put a check (√) beside the words that are spelled correctly. Rewrite the misspelled words correctly under the spelling rule that applies. Then, add all the words with a check to each list under the rules.

percievable	conveneince	decieive	riemburse	height
mischeif	greivous	hygiene	relieve	vareity
asthietic	foreign	retreive	efficeint	consceintious
siege	propreity	anxeity	neither	disbeleif
consceince	soceity	expereince	financeir	sufficeint
decietful	obedeince	liesure	speceis	sieve

"*i* before *e*"	"except after *c*"	"sounds like *a*"	Exceptions
_____	_____	_____	_____
_____	_____	_____	_____
_____	_____	_____	_____
_____	_____	_____	_____
_____	_____	_____	_____
_____	_____	_____	_____
_____	_____	_____	_____
_____	_____	_____	_____
_____	_____	_____	_____
_____	_____	_____	_____

B. Add ten more words to each category.

"*i* before *e*"	"except after *c*"	"sounded like *a*"	Exceptions
_____	_____	_____	_____
_____	_____	_____	_____
_____	_____	_____	_____
_____	_____	_____	_____
_____	_____	_____	_____
_____	_____	_____	_____
_____	_____	_____	_____
_____	_____	_____	_____

Spelling Practice 10: Commonly Misspelled Words

Words containing vowel pairs are often misspelled. Some words follow spelling rules, for example, words with *ei* and *ie*. Other words do not follow spelling rules and the spelling must be memorized.

A. Put a check (√) beside words spelled correctly. Rewrite the misspelled words correctly. Check your spelling in a dictionary.

1. alliance _____
2. niave _____
3. burial _____
4. recriut _____
5. vengaence _____
6. endeavor _____
7. espinage _____
8. giudance _____
9. cruelty _____
10. liquify _____
11. pagaent _____
12. villian _____
13. camuflage _____
14. initative _____
15. guage _____
16. parliament _____
17. marrige _____
18. biscit _____
19. nusance _____
20. conscous _____
21. buolevard _____
22. prarie _____
23. forfit _____
24. allegaince _____
25. tortiose _____
26. minature _____
27. sergent _____
28. mosqiuto _____
29. paesant _____
30. buraeucrat _____

B. Write each word in Exercise A under the heading of the vowel pair.

ai	ia	ui	ea	io/iou	ue	ou	au/eau	ei	oi

_____

_____

_____

_____

_____

_____

_____

_____

_____

_____

_____

_____

_____

_____

Name _____ Date _____

Spelling Practice Review

A. Circle the letter before the correct spelling of the word in each row across.

1. a. percieved   b. perceived   c. perseived   d. persieved
2. a. imeddiate   b. imediate   c. immeddiate   d. immediate
3. a. acheivement   b. achievement   c. acheivment   d. acheevment
4. a. terain   b. terrain   c. terraine   d. tearain
5. a. nuecleus   b. nuecleuss   c. nucleus   d. nucleeus
6. a. notiseble   b. notisabel   c. noticable   d. noticeable
7. a. embarasment   b. embarrasment   c. embarrassment   d. embarassment
8. a. proficent   b. proficient   c. proficeint   d. profficient
9. a. foureign   b. fourain   c. foreign   d. forain
10. a. parliment   b. parliament   c. pairliment   d. parrliment
11. a. accessible   b. accesible   c. accessable   d. accesable
12. a. tyranical   b. tyrannycal   c. tyrannical   d. tyrannicle
13. a. vengence   b. vengaence   c. vengance   d. vengeance
14. a. eficiency   b. eficciency   c. eficienncy   d. efficiency
15. a. endeavor   b. endevor   c. endevour   d. endevourr
16. a. initially   b. inittially   c. inittialy   d. inittally
17. a. convienance   b. convenience   c. convienence   d. conveniance
18. a. bureaucrat   b. beaurocrat   c. buorocrat   d. beuroucrat
19. a. pesant   b. pessant   c. peasant   d.peasent
20. a. conscientous   b. conscientious   c. consclenntious   d. connscientous

B. Underline the words that are misspelled and rewrite them correctly at the end of each sentence.

1. When we reached the Canadian border, it became aparant that we had made a collosial mistake in our navigation.

_____

_____

2. The counseler said there is really no need to be anxous about adolescance.

_____

_____

3. Only in chemistry lab is it permisable to liquify objects with acid.

_____

_____

4. The members of the aliance wore their camoflage uniforms to the commisions ceremony.

_____

_____

5. When describing differant windows, it is important to distingiush between transparant and translusent.

_____

_____

ANSWERS

ANSWERS

Vocabulary Practice 1: Prefixes (p. 1)

A. 1. audible
2. coherent
3. noble
4. partial
5. reparable
6. eligible
7. literate
8. mutable
9. reverent
10. relevant

B. 1. irreparable
2. inaudible
3. irreverent
4. incoherent
5. impartial
6. ignoble
7. immutable
8. illiterate
9. irrelevant
10. ineligible

Vocabulary Practice 2: Prefixes (p. 2)

A. 1. malpractice
2. malcontent
3. misdemeanor
4. miscalculation
5. maladroit
6. misnomer
7. misinterpreted
8. misadventure
9. malfunctioning
10. misshapen

B. 1. mis nomer
2. mis shapen
3. mis interpreted
4. mal functioning
5. mis demeanor
6. mal practice
7. mis adventure
8. mis calculation
9. mal adroit
10. mal content

C. maladjusted
malevolent
malnutrition
misbehave
misappropriate

Vocabulary Practice 3: Prefixes (p. 3)

A. 1. synchronize
2. systemic
3. syndrome
4. symbiotic
5. symphysis
6. systematic
7. symposium
8. symmetry
9. synergy
10. synthesis

B. 1. symbiotic
2. synergy
3. systematic
4. synthesis
5. symposium
6. synchronized
7. systemic
8. symphysis
9. syndrome
10. symmetry

C. symptom
symphony
sympathy
symbolism
syndicate
synergism
synonym
synopsis
systematize
systole

Vocabulary Practice 4: Prefixes (p. 4)

A. 1. climax   anticlimax (Sample response)
2. diction   contradiction
3. productive   counterproductive
4. indication   contraindication
5. sign   countersign
6. thesis   antithesis
7. charged   countercharged
8. -versy   controversy
9. measure   countermeasure
10. intelligence   counterintelligence

B. 1. counterproductive
2. counterintelligence
3. controversy
4. anticlimax
5. countermeasures
6. countersign
7. antithesis
8. contraindication
9. contradiction
10. countercharged

Vocabulary Practice 5: Suffixes (p. 5)

A. 1. fallible   capable of being mistaken
2. palpable   that can be touched or handled; easily perceived by the senses
3. delectable   very pleasing; delicious
4. exhaustible   able to be completely used up or emptied
5. laudable   worthy of praise
6. potable   fit to drink
7. audible   loud enough to be heard
8. pliable   easily bent or molded
9. palatable   pleasant or acceptable to the taste
10. despicable   deserving to be looked down upon with contempt

B. 1. despicable
2. potable
3. fallible
4. delectable
5. palpable
6. exhaustible
7. laudable
8. audible
9. pliable
10. delectable

Vocabulary Practice 6: Suffixes (p. 6)

A. 1. pithy
2. acrimonious
3. porous
4. cumbersome
5. vacuous
6. billowy
7. loathsome
8. frugally
9. precipitous
10. copiously

B. 1. *loathe* and *some*   "full of" detesting (Sample response)
2. *pith* and *y*   "full of" soft, spongy tissue
3. *precipice* and *ous*   "like" a precipice
4. *frugal* and *ly*   "like" stingy
5. *cumber* and *some*   "full of" obstruction
6. *billow* and *y*   "like" swelling or surging
7. *vacuum* and *ous*   "full of" emptiness
8. *acrimony* and *ous*   "full of" bitterness
9. *copious* and *ly*   "like" abundance
10. *pores* and *ous*   "like" a tiny opening

C. partially
coherently
chilly
wispy
worrisome
tiresome
joyous
gelatinous

Vocabulary Practice 7: Suffixes (p. 7)

A. 1. internship
2. adeptness
3. platitude
4. admonishment
5. rectitude
6. enhancement
7. adroitness
8. impoverishment
9. disbandment
10. stewardship

B. 1. internship (Sample response)
  2. disbandment
  3. adroitness
  4. rectitude
  5. stewardship
  6. impoverishment
  7. internship
  8. enhancement
  9. admonishment
  10. adeptness

Vocabulary Practice 8: Combining Forms (p. 8)

A. 1. paleontology
  2. ichthyology
  3. phonology
  4. pharmacology
  5. ideology
  6. sociology
  7. criminology
  8. physiology
  9. immunology
  10. anthropology
  11. chronology
  12. terminology
  13. genealogy
  14. lexicology
  15. dermatology

B. (Sentences are sample responses.)
  1. People who study paleontology discover fossils.
  2. Students of ichthyology might research salmon migration.
  3. Phonology is the study of speech sounds.
  4. Pharmacists study pharmacology, the science dealing with the effects of drugs on living organisms.
  5. A scholar might write about the ideology of a religion.
  6. Those who study sociology often become doctors.
  7. People who work in criminology are police and detectives.
  8. Physiology is a course of study for medical students.
  9. Immunology is a study for doctors and scientists who find cures for diseases.

10. It's fun to study genealogy to learn about one's ancestry.

Vocabulary Practice 9: Word Roots (p. 9)

A. 1. repel means "drive away"
  2. recurrent means "take place again"
  3. impulse means "push"
  4. discursive means "running"
  5. propel means "push"
  6. incur means "cause to take place"
  7. compel means "push to do something"
  8. curriculum means "running of a course"
  9. expulsion means "pushing out"
  10. concurrent means "running at the same time"

B. expel means "to drive out"
  impel means "to push, drive or move forward"
  current means "now in progress"
  impulsive means "likely to act on impulse"
  pulsate means "to beat rhythmically, as the heart"
  pulse means "any rhythmical beat or signal"
  repellent means "that which pushes away or drives back"
  recur means "to return or occur again"
  cursive means "flowing; not disconnected"
  occurrence means "an event or incidence"
  excursion means "a short trip, returning to the point of departure"
  concur means "happening together"
  expulsion means "a facing out"
  compulsion means "a driving force; coercion"
  repulse means "to drive back, as an attack"
  repulsion means "a strong dislike or distaste"
  repulsive means "causing strong dislike or aversion"

Answer to Question: Knowing the root form helps to unlock the meaning of unfamiliar words with the same root.

Vocabulary Practice 10: Word Roots (p. 10)

A. 1. catalogue   brochure
  2. eloquent   well-spoken
  3. loquacious   talkative

4. vociferous noisy
5. convocation assembly
6. prologue introduction
7. monologue speech
8. dictum declaration
9. edict order
10. colloquial conversational

B. (Sentences are sample responses.)

1. People were very upset with the indictment against the civil leader.
2. The invocation was a plea for world peace.
3. The epilogue gave the author's explanation of the conclusion.
4. Hamlet's soliloquy is often quoted by people in a decision-making situation.
5. One might need an advocate when in the hospital.

Vocabulary Practice 11: Word Roots (p. 11)

A. 1. f 2. i 3. g 4. h 5. j 6. a 7. c 8. b 9. e 10. d

B. 1. contention
2. retaining
3. tenure
4. detention
5. contain

6. extend
7. tensile
8. tenacity
9. distend
10. portended

C. (Sentences are sample responses.)

1. The teacher gave us a deadline extension for writing the term paper.
2. Children watched the balloons distending as we filled them with water for the contest!
3. Troop containment was the first step toward peace negotiations.
4. Concert hall management will oversee the retention of all lost property.
5. Mr. Hobbs, the principal, will detain anyone defacing school property.
6. The river began to distend with several inches of rain during the hurricane.
7. Despite setbacks, Willa was tenacious and eventually achieved her goal.
8. The professor's tenure was upheld after he published a controversial book.
9. One candidate will contend the incumbent's spending policies in a debate.
10. We extended our vacation because we were enjoying the island so much.

Vocabulary Practice 12: Word Roots (p. 12)
A.

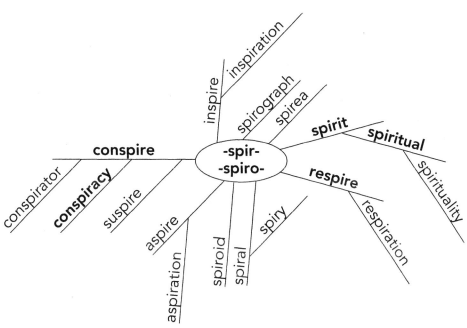

B. 1. *atmosphere*: sphere of air or gases

   2. *ecosphere*: a house for living things

   3. *ionosphere*: sphere of electronically charged atoms

   4. *biosphere*: sphere where life occurs

   5. *bathysphere*: sphere that is used in the deep sea

Other words:

   1. *mesosphere*: the zone 34–50 miles above the earth

   2. *stratosphere*: the atmospheric zone 12–31 miles above the earth

   3. *thermosphere*: the zone that begins at 53 miles above the earth, characterized by a rise in temperature with increasing altitude

   4. *troposphere*: the zone that is characterized by water vapor, vertical winds, and decreasing temperature with increasing altitude

Vocabulary Practice 13: Word Roots (p. 13)

A. 1. translucent
2. photons
3. illuminati
4. pellucid
5. luminary
6. photogenic
7. phototropism
8. lucid
9. elucidate
10. luminescence

B. 1. lucid
2. translucent
3. luminescence
4. phototropism
5. illuminati
6. elucidate
7. pellucid
8. photogenic
9. luminary
10. photon

C. -luc-   lucidity

    -lum-   luminous

    -photo-   telephoto

Vocabulary Practice 14: Synonyms (p. 14)

A. 1. increase
2. gratify
3. develop
4. annoyed
5. balance
6. adventure
7. disappear
8. inscription
9. intrude
10. unity

B. 1. stabilize
2. augment
3. venture
4. epitaph
5. indulge
6. solidarity
7. cultivate
8. encroach
9. dissipate
10. indignant

Vocabulary Practice 15: Synonyms (p. 15)

A. 1. hidden
2. blissfulness
3. barrier
4. disorderly
5. conflicting
6. astute
7. burdensome
8. cunning
9. mortal
10. uncertainty

B. (Sentences are sample responses.)

1. *boisterous* party guests

   The boisterous party guests were asked to leave by the hostess.

2. *sagacious* elderly man

   A sagacious elderly man entertained the children with stories that taught them many aspects of good behavior.

3. bride's *felicity*

   The bride's felicity was apparent and shared by all the wedding guests.

4. *repugnant* odor

   We noticed a repugnant odor at the ocean at low tide.

5. unexpected *hindrance*

   The state highway had unexpected hindrances which delayed our planned arrival.

6. *esoteric* research paper

   We listened politely for two hours to the professor read his esoteric research paper.

7. *dying* foliage

   In the fall, the gardener removed all the dying foliage and replaced it with new shrubs.

8. job applicant's *quandary*

   The job applicant's quandary was resolved when one offer was withdrawn because the position was canceled.

9. *furtive* glances

   When asked about plans for the party, Patti and Peggy exchanged furtive glances.

10. *unwieldy* furniture

    Excellent movers were able to bring in and place the unwieldy furniture.

C. (Sentences are sample responses.)

1. We looked for hidden treasure in the attic.

2. Blissfulness was evident on the faces of the vacationing families.

3. Not having a car was a barrier to Carmen's getting a summer job.

4. People in line to have pictures became disorderly when the photographer was more than one hour late.

5. Conflicting regulations in the dormitory caused turmoil and misconduct.

6. The astute store manager resolved the issue before it became a crisis.

7. Marty discussed some burdensome matters including budgets with the office staff.

8. With cunning, the child outsmarted his older brother and got the extra dessert.

9. The soldier received a mortal wound and said his last words to the nurse aiding him.

10. In his uncertainty, Julio took the wrong turn on the highway and drove a distance from his intended destination.

Vocabulary Practice 16: Synonyms (p. 16)

A. 1. accumulate:: a
   2. agreement:: a
   3. admission:: b
   4. watch:: b
   5. analyze:: b
   6. serious:: a
   7. forgive:: a
   8. restrict:: c
   9. explain:: b
   10. criminal:: b

B. 1. confuse
   2. belittle
   3. unaffected
   4. uncertain
   5. uncommunicative

C. 1. crush
   2. careful
   3. immature
   4. criticizing
   5. dull

Vocabulary Practice 17: Antonyms (p. 17)

A. 1. aggressive, amicable (Sample response)
   2. slovenly   fastidious
   3. unpretentious   arrogant
   4. generous   miserly
   5. incompetent   adept
   6. disingenuous   candid
   7. solution   conundrum
   8. worst   optimal
   9. heavy   slender
   10. unproductive   prolific

B. (Sentences are sample responses.)

1. The *arrogant* Hollywood actor was very humble in person.

2. The community's *conundrum* was knowing how to meet the needs of all the senior citizens.

3. Shirley finally found a tailor who is *adept* at sewing a sequined gown.

4. The college was fortunate to have as a graduate a *charitable* billionaire.

5. The two friends had an *amicable* argument and laughed later.

Vocabulary Practice 18: Antonyms (p. 18)

A. 1. plausible
  2. mundane
  3. insatiable
  4. innumerable
  5. sanguine
  6. peevish
  7. expedient
  8. neophyte
  9. motley
  10. taper

B. 1. expedient, it is impractical to carry cash
  2. mundane, not choose another unusual movie for a long time
  3. insatiable, her usually content manner when eating
  4. peevish, she gave her excuses to her good-natured grandmother
  5. neophyte, he is a professional of long experience
  6. sanguine, pessimistic news they've had recently
  7. plausible, accomplished the impossible by scoring a touchdown in the last second of the game
  8. taper, widen at the mouth
  9. innumerable, that the few I could see were all there were
  10. motley, identical appearance of the host and hostess

Vocabulary Practice 19: Antonyms (p. 19)

A. 1. resolute
  2. auspicious
  3. insufficient
  4. destitute
  5. effervescent
  6. excessive
  7. innocuous
  8. pliable
  9. sterile
  10. unkempt

B. 1. insufficient, deficient, inadequate
  2. flat, despondent, depressed, lifeless
  3. unfavorable, hopeless, pessimistic
  4. doubtful, hesitating, wavering
  5. injurious, adverse, destructive

Vocabulary Practice 20: Synonym and Antonym Review (p. 20)

A. 1. countless
  2. mystery
  3. taciturn
  4. haughty
  5. certain
  6. sharp
  7. necessary
  8. slender
  9. earthly
  10. assorted
  11. productive
  12. foolish
  13. indefinite
  14. sanitary
  15. solution

B. 1. immeasurable: infinite
  2. puzzle: riddle
  3. reticent: forward
  4. disdainful: contemptuous
  5. sure: doubtful
  6. blunt: pointed
  7. essential: unimportant
  8. slim: slight
  9. worldly: mundane
  10. various: mixed
  11. fruitful: thriving
  12. judicious: prudent
  13. undecided: wavering
  14. immaculate: fastidious
  15. uncertainty: resolution

Vocabulary Practice 21: Analogies (p. 21)

A. 1. trying
  2. death
  3. knowledge
  4. destruction
  5. transport
  6. stabilize
  7. confusion
  8. support
  9. declare
  10. stress

B. 1. rest

    2. sterilize

    3. productivity

    4. cut

    5. promotion

C. DRINK:QUENCHES::FOOD:NOURISHES

    Cause and Effect

    CHALK:CHALKBOARD::PAINT:CANVAS

    Function

Vocabulary Practice 22: Analogies (p. 22)

A. 1. congress

    2. exercise

    3. escalator

    4. cake

    5. language

    6. school

    7. poem

    8. weather

    9. wall

    10. communication

B. 1. fasten

    2. mineral

    3. ship

    4. flexibility

    5. wood

C. Answers for Exercise A

    1. part-to-whole

    2. type of

    3. part-to-whole

    4. part-to-whole

    5. type of

    6. part-to-whole

    7. type of

    8. type of

    9. part-to-whole

    10. type of

Answers for Exercise B

    1. function

    2. type of

    3. part-to-whole

    4. function

    5. type of

Vocabulary Practice 23: Analogies (p. 23)

A. 1. fiction

    2. blunt

    3. fruit

    4. savings

    5. diminish

    6. novice

    7. warmth

    8. torso

    9. kind

    10. disinfect

B. 1. infallible: imperfect

    2. moisture: dampness

    3. dictum: instruct

    4. depressed: elated

    5. member: committee

C. Answers for Exercise A

    1. type of

    2. synonyms

    3. type of

    4. cause and effect

    5. antonyms

    6. synonyms

    7. function

    8. part-to-whole

    9. antonyms

    10. function

Answers for Exercise B

    1. synonyms

    2. cause and effect

    3. function

    4. antonyms

    5. part-to-whole

Vocabulary Practice 24: Connotations and Denotations (p. 24)

A. 1. *contrite* means "feeling remorse for having done wrong"

    2. *cowardly* means "shamefully" or "fearfully"

    3. *ornate* means "heavily adorned" or "showy"

    4. *strife* means "the act of striving with another; quarreling or fighting"

    5. *vacillate* means "to sway to and fro; to waver or show indecision"

    6. *recant* means "to withdraw; to renounce in a formal way"

    7. *lassitude* means "a state of feeling tired and listless"

    8. *opulent* means "very wealthy or rich; characterized by abundance"

9. *melancholy* means "sadness and depression of spirits; gloomy"

10. *plaintiveness* means "expressing sorrow; mournful"

B.
1. retract	repudiate
2. spineless	afraid
3. hesitate	falter
4. penitent	humbled
5. moodiness	despair
6. gaudy	decorated
7. warfare	unrest
8. disconsolate	mournful
9. affluent	magnificent
10. weariness	exhaustion

C. (Sentences are sample responses.)

1. The politician decided to retract his statement about his opponent.

2. Perpetrators of atrocious crimes are considered spineless and despicable.

3. The contest winners did not hesitate when asked to choose their prizes.

4. While standing before the judge, the kidnapper was penitent and remorseful.

5. Elderly people are often in despair when stricken with long-term illness.

6. For the street fair, homes were adorned in bunting of gaudy colors.

7. When the tornado devastated the city, a situation of unrest and anxiety erupted.

8. Family members were disconsolate when they could not reach stranded relatives.

9. The affluent community raised enough money to sustain relief efforts.

10. When the teacher noticed apathy in her students, she discussed her expectations for their performance.

Vocabulary Practice 25: Connotations and Denotations (p. 25)

A.
1.	a. barren	b. commonplace
2.	a. soothe	b. conciliate
3.	a. earsplitting	b. raucous
4.	a. playful	b. degenerate
5.	a. contrived	b. fabricated
6.	a. imitate	b. rival
7.	a. uncover	b. betray
8.	a. negligence	b. leniency
9.	a. acute	b. penetrating
10.	a. tenacious	b. continuous

B.
1. barren: sterile, infertile
commonplace: average, general

2. soothe: calm, pacify
conciliate: appease, placate

3. raucous: grating, harsh
earsplitting: blaring, roaring

4. playful: frisky, mischievous
degenerate: corrupt, reprehensible

5. contrived: forced, strained
fabricated: concocted, contrived

6. imitate: copy, model
rival: challenge, approximate

7. uncover: disclose, show
betray: expose, reveal

8. leniency: charity, mercy
negligence: laxity, slackness

9. penetrating: sharp, incisive
acute: keen, perceptive

10. tenacious: headstrong, obstinate
continuous: ceaseless, constant

Vocabulary Practice 26: Connotations and Denotations (p. 26)

A.
1. gentle
2. polite
3. apprehensive
4. quiet
5. unassuming
6. timid
7. deferential
8. withdrawn
9. obliging
10. docile
11. sedate
12. meek
13. respectful
14. shy
15. submissive

B. (Sample response.)

Jessica was so quiet during dinner that everyone forgot she was at the table. Her gentle demeanor receded into the background when she was among more outgoing personalities. As a child, Jessica was shy and withdrawn. In school, her friends spoke of her as modest and polite. When she talked to adults, she was always respectful. Jessica fit the description of a sedate personality.

Vocabulary Practice 27: Commonly Misused Words (p. 27)

A. 1. *rein* means "a narrow leather strap attached to the bit in a horse's mouth to control the animal"

reign means "the period of rule; royal power"

rain means "water falling to the earth"

2. *discreet* means "careful about what one says or does"

discrete means "separate and distinct;" "unrelated"

3. *stationery* means "paper and other writing materials"

stationary means "fixed;" "not moving"

4. *compliment* means "a formal expression of courtesy or respect, as in praise"

complement means "something added to complete a whole; that which brings to perfection"

5. *waiver* means "the act of relinquishing voluntarily"

waver means "to swing or sway to and fro"

6. *straight* means "having the same direction throughout its length"

strait means "a waterway connecting two large bodies of water; difficulty; distress" (usually plural)

7. *root* means "the part of a plant, usually below ground"

route means "a road or course for travel, usually a highway"

8. *site* means "the place where something is, was, or is to be"

cite means "to quote a passage"

sight means "something seen; a view"

9. *capital* means "the most important or most serious"

capitol means "the building in which a State legislature meets"

10. *aid* means "help or assistance"

aide means "an assistant"

B. 1. discreet
2. compliment
3. reign
4. waiver
5. site

C. (Sentences are sample responses.)

1. The policeman adjusted the rein in his horse's mouth.
2. A heavy rain began just before the picnic.
3. The package contained ten discrete items from the sunken ship.
4. Fine stationery is a pleasure to use and receive.

A stationary mailbox was put on the corner.
5. Grandmother's hat complemented her outfit.
6. "Stand straight and tall," said Mother.

An oil tanker sailed through the straits and into the open sea.
7. The plant sprouted a new root and grew healthy.

What route will you take home today?
8. At the end of the day, the sunset was a beautiful sight.

The children's father cited instances of overspending and decided not to increase allowances.
9. The teacher took points off the term paper for missing capital letters.

Have you visited the capitol building in your state?
10. Foreign countries rely on aid from the Red Cross in times of disaster.

An aide arrived to help the new patient.

Vocabulary Practice 28: Commonly Misused Words (p. 28)

A.
1.	assume	presume
2.	proven	proved
3.	ceremonial	ceremonious
4.	aggravate	irritate
5.	aural	oral

B.
1.	a. assumed	b. presume
2.	a. proved	b. proven
3.	a. ceremonious	b. ceremonial
4.	a. aggravates	b. irritate
5.	a. oral	b. aural

C. 1. *allusion* means "an indirect reference; a casual mention"

The allusion to a raise by the supervisor boosted employee morale.

2. *illusion* means "a false idea or conception"

Unfortunately, the promise of a skiing vacation was an advertising illusion.

3. *quote* means "to repeat or reproduce words from a source"

The speaker quoted the author of an historical novel.

4. *quotation* means "the words or passage quoted"

A quotation from a respected author supported the speaker's argument.

Vocabulary Practice 29: Commonly Misused Words (p. 29)

A.

1. loath	elder
2. raise	uninterested
3. device	preclude
4. emigrate	compared with
5. loathed	prevented
6. skeptical	cynical
7. rising	immigrate
8. differ with	devise
9. differ from	older
10. compared to	disinterested

B. (Sample response)

Lauren loathed the color green, a fact that prevented her from being a successful landscape painter. Her mother's elder sister was a well-known artist who differed with Lauren's adamant avoidance of green in her palette. But Lauren devised a unique palette to paint landscape without requiring the color green.

Vocabulary Practice 30: Specialized Vocabulary (p. 30)

A.
1. i Hebrew
2. s Old English
3. p Sanskrit
4. j Greek
5. h Dutch
6. t Persian
7. d Greek
8. n Egyptian
9. a Sanskrit
10. g Rhaeto-Romanic
11. c American Spanish
12. b Germanic
13. o Arabic
14. q Middle High German
15. e French
16. k Indo-European
17. r Middle Dutch
18. m Old Norse
19. l Persian
20. f Old Slavic

B. (five responses)
1. *bazaar* Arabic; means "a market or street of shops and stalls; a shop for selling various kinds of goods"
2. *oasis* Coptic; means "a fertile place in a desert, because of presence of water" (original word meant "fertile spot")
3. *mission* Avestan; means "a sending out or being sent out with authority to perform a service" (original word meant "cast down")
4. *grapple* Old French; means "coming to grips; hand-to-hand fight" (from grapnel meaning "an iron bar with claws at the end for holding things")
5. *bonanza* Spanish; means "any source of great wealth or profits"
6. *pecan* American Indian; means "an olive-shaped edible nut with a thin, smooth shell"
7. *cookie* Dutch; means "a small sweet cake, usually flat, often crisp"
8. *paradise* Persian; means "a place of perfect contentment or beauty"
9. *cargo* Spanish; means "the load of commodities carried by ship, plane, truck, etc."
10. *magazine* Arabic; means "a place of storage"

Vocabulary Practice 31: Specialized Vocabulary (p. 31)

A.
1. *aneurysm* means "a sac formed by enlargement of an artery wall, vein, or the heart"
2. *deposition* means "removal from office or position of power; the act of testifying"
3. *misdemeanor* means "in law, a minor offense"
4. *antibiotic* means "a chemical substance that inhibits growth of bacteria"
5. *histology* means "a branch of biology concerned with the structure of tissues"

6. *ophthalmologist* means "one who deals with the branch of medicine related to the eye"

7. *appellate court* means "in law, the court having jurisdiction to review appeals"

8. *internist* means "a doctor who specializes in internal medicine"

9. *paralysis* means "a partial or complete loss, or temporary interruption of body function"

10. *assault* means "a violent attack, either physical or verbal"

11. *larceny* means "the taking of personal property without consent"

12. *plagiarism* means "an idea or words that have been taken from another and passed off as one's own"

13. *clinic* means "the teaching of medicine by treating patients in the presence of students"

14. *libel* means "any false and malicious written or printed statement, tending to injure a person in any way"

15. *specialist* means "a person who concentrates in a particular field of study or professional work"

B.

Medical		Legal	
aneurysm	internist	deposition	larceny
antibiotic	paralysis	misdemeanor	plagiarism
histology	clinic	appellate court	libel
ophthalmologist	specialist	assault	specialist

Spelling Practice 1: Words With *ei* and *ie* (p. 32)

A.

i before e	Except after c	Sounds like an *a*	Exception
pierce	deceive	freight	counterfeit
relieve	perceive	inveigh	weird
achieve	conceivable	weight	neither
besiege	conceit	heinous	leisure
grievous	receipt	reign	conscience
chieftain			efficient
			proficient
			heiress

B. 1. inveigh
2. proficient
3. grievous
4. conceivable
5. mischievous
6. heinous
7. counterfeit
8. perceive
9. besiege
10. conscience

Spelling Practice 2: Final e With Suffixes
(p. 33)

A. 1. introspectively
2. porous
3. enveloping
4. consolable
5. foreboding
6. discouragement
7. obtusely
8. peaceful
9. manageable

10. furtively
11. acknowledgment
12. adventurous
13. salvageable
14. engagement
15. interloping
16. coarsest
17. dredging
18. infringement
19. rarest
20. tasteful

B. 1. immeasurable   1
  2. atonement   3
  3. grudging   3
  4. perpetuating   1
  5. tasteful   2
  6. sparest   1
  7. outrageous   4
  8. doting   1
  9. valuable   4
  10. sedately   2

Spelling Practice 3: Final y With Suffixes
(p. 34)

A. 1. simplifying
2. melodious
3. annoyance
4. shabbily
5. dizziness
6. coyness
7. unifying
8. reliant
9. defraying
10. tardiness
11. justifiable
12. betrayer
13. accompanying
14. satisfactorily
15. messiness
16. pitied
17. variant
18. joyous
19. fortifiable
20. glorious
21. defiance
22. bountiful
23. babyish

24. obeying
25. employer
26. solidifying
27. dutiful
28. signified
29. haughtiness
30. cheerily

B.   **Change _y_ to _i_**   **Retain _y_**

	Change _y_ to _i_	Retain _y_
1.	melodious	simplifying
2.	shabbily	annoyance
3.	dizziness	coyness
4.	reliant	unifying
5.	tardiness	defraying
6.	justifiable	betrayer
7.	satisfactorily	accompanying
8.	messiness	joyous
9.	pitied	babyish
10.	variant	obeying
11.	fortifiable	employer
12.	glorious	solidifying
13.	defiance	
14.	bountiful	
15.	dutiful	
16.	signified	
17.	haughtiness	
18.	cheerily	

Spelling Practice 4: Double the Final Consonant (pp. 35–36)

A. 1. rebelled
2. commitment
3. monogramming
4. occurring
5. casually
6. benefited
7. retractable
8. tranquilly
9. disappointment
10. preferable
11. container
12. programmed
13. discovery
14. kidnapper
15. keenness
16. preening
17. gripped
18. maneuverable

19. wallowing
20. outfitted
21. legally
22. conferred
23. compatible
24. diagramming
25. regrettable
26. maintaining
27. disbanded
28. tautness
29. plainly
30. deferred

B.

Rule 1	Rule 2	Rule 3	Rule 4
rebelled	casually	gripped	retractable
commitment	tranquilly		disappointment
monogramming	container		disbanded
occurring	keenness		
benefited	preening		
preferable	legally		
programmed	maintaining		
discovery	tautness		
kidnapper	plainly		
maneuverable			
wallowing			
outfitted			
conferred			
compatible			
diagramming			
regrettable			
deferred			

C.

Rule 1	Rule 2	Rule 3	Rule 4
compelled	ideally	wrapped	contentment
submitted	greenness	grinning	swiftly
deferring	freely	crabby	grounded
prohibited	sprouted	flawless	soundness
employment	especially	fixed	resigned
recoverable	creamy	chipper	checking
exhibiting	fashionable	gritty	tufted
hallowed	loudness	tanning	surrounding
hovering	steeped	taxing	assignment
forgotten	hauling	scrubbing	strictly

Spelling Practice 5: Words Ending in -al, -cal, and -cle (p. 37)

A.

-cal* or *-cle

1. chemical
2. chronicle
3. practical
4. economical
5. monocle
6. particle
7. cubicle
8. comical
9. whimsical
10. radical

-al

1. ceremonial
2. sensual
3. testimonial
4. denial
5. dismissal
6. occasional
7. racial
8. industrial
9. exceptional
10. educational

B. 1. educational
   2. comical
   3. practical
   4. occasional
   5. Testimonials

C. Rule 1

instrumental
renewal
perusal
rehearsal
normal

Rule 2

matrimonial
trial
burial
colonial
familial

Rule 3

historical
biological
typical
mythological
article

Spelling Practice 6: Words Ending in -cy and -sy (p. 38)

A. 1. deficiency
   2. autocracy
   3. immediacy
   4. dependency
   5. efficiency
   6. prophecy and prophesy
   7. competency
   8. intimacy
   9. transcendency
   10. delinquency
   11. adequacy
   12. relevancy
   13. delicacy
   14. buoyancy
   15. truancy

B. 1. ecstasy
   2. bureaucracy
   3. √
   4. tendency
   5. embassy
   6. candidacy
   7. √
   8. hypocrisy
   9. fantasy
   10. intricacy
   11. √
   12. discrepancy
   13. advocacy
   14. obstinacy
   15. √

Spelling Practice 7: Words Ending in *-ance, -ence, -ant,* and *-ent* (pp. 39–40)

A.

-ance	*-ant*
defiance	defiant
attendance	attendant
acquaintance	————
vigilance	vigilant
maintenance	————

-ence	*-ent*
reverence	reverent
acquiescence	acquiescent
correspondence	correspondent
insistence	insistent
reminiscence	reminiscent
difference	different
inference	————
residence	resident
indulgence	indulgent

B.
1. acquaintance
2. tolerant
3. √
4. reluctant
5. permanence
6. patience
7. corpulent
8. compliance
9. ordinance
10. √
11. translucent
12. magnificent
13. conductance
14. resplendent
15. independent
16. √
17. indignant
18. pertinent
19. insolence
20. √
21. ascendance
22. malevolent
23. attendance
24. superintendent
25. transcendence
26. impatient
27. determinant
28. condescendence
29. presence
30. dissonant

C.
1. ordinance
2. dissonant
3. impatient
4. brilliance
5. superintendent
6. conductance
7. elegant
8. Ambience
9. attendance
10. compliance
11. translucent
12. transcendence
13. presence
14. Resplendent
15. independent

Spelling Practice 8: Commonly Misspelled Words

A.
1. cellar, accessible
2. innocent, accusations
3. fission, efficient
4. terrain
5. curriculum, successfully
6. intelligence
7. appearance, professor, brilliant
8. necessary, irreparable
9. occasionally
10. embarrassment, forgetting, stellar
11. sufficient
12. penicillin, vaccines
13. grammatically, fundamentally
14. suppress, stubbornness
15. Tomorrow, privilege

B.
1. cellar, accessible, innocent, accusations, fission, efficient, terrain, curriculum, successfully, intelligence, appearance, professor, brilliant, necessary, irreparable, occasionally, embarrassment, forgetting, stellar, sufficient, penicillin, vaccines, grammatically, fundamentally, suppress, stubbornness, tomorrow

Spelling Practice 9: Commonly Misspelled Words

A.

i before e	except after c	sounds like a	Exceptions
1. mischief	perceivable	weight	conscience
2. convenience	deceitful		society
3. grievous	deceive		leisure
4. propriety			reimburse
5. obedience			efficient
6. retrieve			neither
7. anxiety			financier
8. experience			species
9. reimburse			conscientious
10. variety			sufficient
11. disbelief			foreign
12. hygiene			height
13. siege			
14. relieve			
15. sieve			

B.

i before e	except after c	sounds like a	Exceptions
1. thief	conceit	eighth	their
2. relief	perceive	vein	ancient
3. achieve	receive	weigh	seize
4. pierce	conceive	reign	caffeine
5. chief	receipt	freight	proficient

Spelling Practice 10: Commonly Misspelled Words

A. 1. √
2. naïve
3. √
4. recruit
5. vengeance
6. √
7. espionage
8. guidance
9. √
10. liquefy
11. pageant
12. villain
13. camouflage
14. initiative
15. gauge
16. √
17. marriage
18. biscuit
19. nuisance
20. conscious
21. boulevard
22. prairie
23. forfeit
24. allegiance
25. tortoise
26. miniature
27. sergeant
28. mosquito
29. peasant
30. bureaucrat

B.

ai	ia	ui	ea
naïve	burial	recruit	vengeance
villain	alliance	guidance	endeavor
prairie	initiative	biscuit	pageant
	parliament	nuisance	sergeant
	marriage	mosquito	peasant
	allegiance		
	miniature		

io/iou	ue	ou	au/eau
espionage	cruelty	boulevard	gauge
conscious	liquefy	camouflage	bureaucrat

ei	oi
forfeit	tortoise

Spelling Practice Review

A. 1. b

2. d

3. b

4. b

5. c

6. d

7. c

8. b

9. c

10. b

11. a

12. c

13. d

14. d

15. a

16. a

17. b

18. a

19. c

20. b

B. 1. apparent, colossal

2. counselor, anxious, adolescence

3. permissible, liquefy

4. alliance, camouflage, commissions

5. different, distinguish, transparent, translucent